W9-BFN-048

BODY and MATURE
BEHAVIOUR

M. Feldenkrais

BODY and MATURE BEHAVIOUR

A STUDY OF ANXIETY, SEX,
GRAVITATION & LEARNING

INTERNATIONAL UNIVERSITIES PRESS, INC.

Madison   Connecticut

CONTENTS

ACKNOWLEDGEMENTS

THE substance of this book was presented before the Association of Scientific Workers at Fairlie, Scotland, in a series of lectures given in 1943–44.

I wish to thank Professor J. D. Bernal, F.R.S., Professor Solly Zuckerman, F.R.S., and his colleague, specialist in posture and growth, for reading the manuscript and for valuable suggestions. I am grateful to my friends Mr. and Mrs. S. Byard, W. Halliday and R. B. Serle for their patient listening, to Dr. G. D. Morgan for clarifying my ideas on some points in psychology.

I am especially grateful to my friend R. B. Serle for repeated reading and correcting of the manuscript and Miss Dorothy Smith for typing it.

I owe a great debt of gratitude to Mrs. Vera F. Salomons and Mrs. Charlotte Nissen whose friendship made this work possible.

M.F.

BM/Moshe,
London, W.C.1.

GLOSSARY

AFFECT, emotional complex associated with a mental state ; the energy of an emotion.

AFFECTIVE, pertaining to a feeling or emotional state.

AMAUROTIC, blind without apparent lesion of the eye but through disease of the optic nerve, spine or brain.

ATLAS, the first cervical vertebra supporting the skull.

AXON, the axis-cylinder of a nerve cell.

CATATONIC, a form of schizophrenia with phases of stupor and excitement.

CHRONAXIE, the specific time required to excite a nervous or muscular element ; the minimum time at which a current is just double the rheobase (minimum producing excitation).

CLONIC, of a spasmodic nature, where rigidity and relaxation succeed each other.

CORTEX, the outer grey layer of the brain.

DENDRITE, tree-shaped process of a nerve cell.

EGO, the part of the mind which recognises and tests reality and is credited with consciousness.

ENDOLYMPH, the fluid contained in the membranous labyrinth of the ear.

EXTEROCEPTIVE, pertaining to the outer field of feeling organs.

ID, primitive mind containing only innate urges.

INTEROCEPTIVE pertaining to the internal feeling receptors.

LABILE, unstable, fluid, liable to change.

LIBIDO, the energy of the sexual drive.

NEUROSIS, a functional disorder of the nervous system.

NYSTAGMUS, an involuntary rapid movement of the eyeball.

ORGASM, the point where erotic excitement becomes involuntary.

OTOLITH, a small stony mass in the membranous vestibule.

pH, hydrogen ion concentration, pH7 is the neutral point, above 7 alkalinity increases, below 7 acidity increases.

PHASIC, contraction, like that in voluntary movements.

PROPRIOCEPTIVE, pertaining to field of feeling organs of the supporting tissue, tendons, ligaments, etc.

PSYCHOSIS, deeper mental disorder ; insanity.

PYRAMIDAL TRACT, a number of fibres descending the spinal cord.

RINGER'S SOLUTION, solution used for perfusing the heart of a frog.

SOLEUS, a muscle extending and rotating the foot.

SOMA, body.

SOMATIC, pertaining to the body.

SPINAL ANIMAL, one in which all the brain above the 2nd cervical nerve has been removed.

SUPER EGO, the part of the mind developed in early life by re repressing frustrated impulses and which monitors the ego.

SYMPATHETIC SYSTEM, also vegetative system, visceral nervous system showing independence of the central nervous system.

SYNAPSE, the region between the processes of two nervous cells.

TELECEPTORS, organs receiving excitation from distant sources.

THALAMUS, a mass of grey matter at the base of the brain.

TONIC CONTRACTION, prolonged contraction like in standing of involuntary origin.

TRANSDUCER, any device transforming energy from one form to another ; a loudspeaker transforming electric energy into sound ; the eye transforming light into nervous impulses, etc.

TRANSFERENCE, displacement of affect from one person to another.

TRAUMATIC, violent enough to produce morbid condition.

TRITON, kind of salamander.

VAGUS, the pneumogastric nerve.

VEGETATIVE SYSTEM *see* SYMPATHETIC.

INTRODUCTION

For a long time we believed ourselves to be essentially different from animals. We believed we had souls, that we were created in the image of God, that the world was created for us and revolved around us. With the development of science, however, and especially with the advent of the theory of evolution we swung steadily round looking for any evidence proving that we were merely animals though complex and highly accomplished. Both views are over-simplifications.

To understand human behaviour we must inquire into the differences as well as the similarities of behaviour. We are so struck by the extensive variety of human behaviour as to make the theory of individual psychologies necessary. Compared with the relative uniformity of even the highest primates, human beings differ so much one from another that the idea of innate individuality forces itself on our minds. At birth the differences of response of the human child are on the whole comparable with those of other animals. Gradually differentiation takes place even in what seem to be quite similar conditions.

Without a clearer understanding of the mechanisms which are behind this apparent wholly innate individuality the problems of behaviour and behaviour disorders lead to great confusion of thought and practice. Thus, no objective inquiry can deny that at least some neurotic symptoms disappear with Yogi practice, hypnotism, auto-suggestion, Christian Science, a visit to Lourdes and a number of other practices, let alone common medical treatment.

Undoubtedly many of these " cures " are superficial and temporary, but by no means all of them ; on the other hand, cures resulting from the most up-to-date scientific methods are subject to the same criticism, except that scientific methods admit failure when there is failure and try to eliminate it. The question, what is it that produces " cure," cannot be answered satisfactorily without understanding the origin and mechanism of the individual response. Even the most modern methods are vague as to how the satisfactory result is achieved. According to Freud's original teaching, cure takes place when an unconscious desire or drive is made conscious and can be rejected by the mature ego. The symptom which owes its existence to an unconscious desire must disappear when the desire loses its unconscious quality. Freud himself later modified his views on the subject.

Many authors consider the transference phenomenon to be responsible for bringing about cure. They stress the importance of reliving affectively the traumatic event with the analyst as the object of love and hatred. Guided by the analyst's objective attitude and his skill the patient is helped in solving his problem.

It remains, however, that cures are brought about by so many divergent methods that the fact of improvement cannot be considered as proof of correctness of theory unless the cures are considerably more consistent and predictable than they are at present.

The history of psychoanalysis started with hypnotism which Freud himself practised and then finally discarded. The present revival of this practice is only an indication of the prevailing lack of clarity of thought.

It may be useful to review briefly the theory behind some of the older, more widely practised methods. In the hypnotic state it was thought an idea could be presented directly to the unconscious. In this state the person, in whom the conscious is inhibited, is capable of feats of strength, memory and other activities. He is able to carry out with perfection acts that are beyond his capacity in the waking state. It would seem therefore that the capacity for perfect doing is present in every man but must remain latent when conscious control is operative. The conscious is therefore a hindrance.

Coué relied expressly on the unconscious to bring about all the desired improvements. He devised several means whereby he could by-pass the conscious control and plant his ideas " directly " in the unconscious. He used the period before sleep when we are half conscious ; whispering into the ear of the sleeping ; rapid repetition—and so forth, with the idea of reaching the unconscious and avoiding the conscious critical faculty which does not believe in this or the other idea of " I can," and rejects them. Once the idea reaches the unconscious it becomes operative. He explained hypnotism as a successful act of auto-suggestion, and denied the importance of the hypnotist's powers.

Here, then, the conscious was thought responsible for all the symptoms, as it sifts and picks the ideas that it presents to the unconscious, where they at once become operative.

This theory is obviously radically opposed to that of psychoanalysis. Coué thought the unconscious an executive power. Once an idea is presented to it, be it pleasant or self-mutilating, like the idea of being unable to use a limb or an organ, it is carried out. An idea must be a pure image completely stripped or void of affect before it can reach the unconscious. Thus the effort of will is a hindrance rather than a means of making oneself do something. Normally, we learn to succeed in presenting the idea in the right way. The divergence of these views from those of Freud is fundamental. The only ground common to the two theories is that the affective content of an idea is a deciding factor ; but the rôles attributed to it and the whole mechanism of psychic life are completely inverted.

The important point, however, is that though Coué's theory appears today to many to be so much muddled thinking, he was a great human benefactor and had to his personal credit innumerable " cures," often " miraculous " ones. Probably not many living therapists can claim a comparable record.

Cures as proof of correctness of theory must be discarded until such time as each failure can be fully explained. The cures are the result of what is actually being done. This is in general so complex that there is room for each theory to point to one or other element of the procedure as the clue to the problem. Psychoanalytic treatment in its infancy also produced cures though the explanation then given was the one Freud himself discarded later. Every method of psychotherapy is correct on one point or other. The problems involved have so many facets that this is possible. They are all wrong in pretending to have solved the whole problem. In that respect psychoanalysis is less guilty and is more scientific in its approach than other teachings.

All the methods, irrespective of their merits, divide into two groups. Those such as hypnotism, auto-suggestion, psychoanalysis and others that grew historically one out of the other, have one thing in common : the belief that once the mind function is set right the somatic or body trouble clears up without further direct effort. In more or less complete opposition to this group is the other, that puts all the emphasis on training the body directly. The Yogi methods and the relaxation methods that grew out of it, breathing methods, certain schools of dancing, all teach mental balance through the physical body. And curiously enough they have a certain measure of undeniable success. It is difficult to make an accurate estimate of the number of people who obtain relief by such practices. Judging by my own observation the number of people who have been helped to arrive at some sort of stable mode of life by these methods is very considerable. There is hardly a neurotic person who has not tried one or another method, often original personal ones, of training himself. Many have managed to obtain sufficient relief to confirm their belief in their own power.

To sum up, it can be said that men believe in the interaction of the mind and the body. Some methods attribute greater fundamental importance to the mind, others to the body. Both views have some grounds for their beliefs. The result is inextricable confusion of thought. And the reason for this confusion is the arbitrary subdivision of life into psychic and physical. Even by assuming that the two are only different aspects of one and the same thing not much is gained practically.

Many attempts were made to do away with this duality for it seemed that the idea had exhausted its fruitfulness and would yield no more. Freud said, though he subsequently made no use of it, that the unconscious is based on the chemistry of physiological processes. It was, however, Pavlov who first succeeded in explaining functions usually considered as involving psychic activity on purely physiological grounds. The theory of conditioned reflexes and the work of Magnus, Speransky and others give grounds for another step forward. They show that a reasonably satisfactory explanation of all psychic and somatic life can be derived from the study of growth of functions of the human frame. This is considered to be a step forward because it explains why all the above-mentioned methods often result in cures, and why more often still there is some sort of improvement and then a relapse. And what is more important, it opens up new horizons and new avenues for inquiry. It would be futile to expect that all these problems can be solved with a new outlook only. There are naturally new questions to be answered.

The most fundamental property of the scientific method is that it always leads up to a point where only experiment, i.e., confronting theory with reality, gives weight to the true argument and discards the others that may have seemed equally or more plausible. It generally brings to light phenomena that were considered trifling and unimportant.

We are not surprised to find that we know in fact very little of the properties of the nervous tissue, and discover with Speransky and his school many unexpected phenomena. For instance, the body reacts physiologically almost as a fundamentally new entity after certain irritations of the nervous system. Especially remarkable is the effect of " massage of the brain," consisting of successive variations of pressure of the cerebrospinal fluid produced by alternating extraction and reintroduction of some of it.

Changes of pressure of the cerebro-spinal fluid are normally produced quite readily and between very wide limits by compression of the jugular veins. Thus many esoteric practices of Judoka and Yogi find physiological basis and can be experimentally justified.

There are, indeed, important masses of the brain which, for all we know about their function, might just as well not be there. Their removal makes only little difference and no single function is completely annihilated. Even the loss of a leg does not destroy the capacity for moving about ; only the rate and the mode of doing are affected. Analogous results are obtained by removal of certain masses of the brain ; this is discussed later. To eliminate the total function, nothing short of total destruction of the body will do.

In all neurotic states we find anxiety, nausea, giddiness, muscular tension, digestive and breathing troubles and sexual disorders of some sort. So long as there is no improvement in these troubles there is no improvement in the general state—and vice-versa. Muscular tension and anxiety are invariably so closely interwoven in all states of emotional disorder that it is difficult to see how any real advancement towards clearer understanding of the nature of cures is possible without greater knowledge of the phenomenon of anxiety.

A number of facts must be brought together to give at least a direction for constructive thought. Lesions destroying exactly the same areas in two adult brains do not cause the same symptoms. The life experience of the brain is in some way written in the cortex. " Even in the excitable motor cortex (Sir Charles P. Symonds, President of the Royal Society of Psychiatry), where functional patterns are relatively stable, it is evident that response depends on individual experience. Whether extension or flexion will take place in a digit depends on what has just happened, not only at this point of the cortex but in the sensory cortex behind it." Emotional tensions affect the cortex via the vegetative nervous system. All neurotic symptoms are intimately connected with and express themselves by affecting the relationship of the person to other persons or society in general.

It is of the greatest importance to be quite clear on what is amenable to human influence. If behaviour means all response to stimulus, we must distinguish between reflex responses which are by definition outside human influence, and those, formed under the influence of environment after birth, which are likely to be influenced by change of environment *a priori*.

A reflex activity is a biological inheritance generally common to a whole group of animals and it is essentially immaterial whether the individual has had any previous experience or not, since the first stimulus will elicit the same response as the second. Subject to the laws governing fatigue of the nervous cell and some other laws, the response is elicited every time the irritation occurs.

Such inheritance is genetic, i.e., handed down to each individual through the genes of the species, and we can do little to alter it unless we can modify the genes of the species. If we could modify the genes we would obtain a new species in which the modified genes would be perpetuated in all subsequent generations.

Any behaviour that is not handed down to subsequent generations in accordance with the general laws of inheritance is not of a genetic character, and is therefore an acquired response or an acquired behaviour. It follows that human behaviour is so essentially acquired that some of our most cherished beliefs unquestionably need revision.

Acquired behaviour is the result of interaction of the genetic entity with its environment. Thus it seems legitimate to assert that, provided the environment can be altered, the acquired behaviour would undergo change. In other words, all characteristic behaviour that does not obey the laws of inheritance is amenable to environmental influence.

The conclusion just reached is rich in consequences, especially if we consider genetic inheritance to embrace complex as well as simple reflexes. For complex sequences or a simultaneous combination of simple reflexes is the physiologist's definition of an instinct.

This important conclusion results then, that true instinctive behaviour alone is impervious to experience and environment. More precisely, only those responses that cannot be elicited after an alteration in the nervous paths concerned are instinctive ; all other behaviour is acquired and has nothing permanent about it but our belief that it is so.

It is in this connection that the study of function and structure relations appears in its full significance. In every case where the actual use made of the body can be shown to account for the physical structure, it becomes certain that the particular shape of the structure, though it may be similar to that of the parent, is still amenable to human influence.

This approach makes it imperative that answers to many problems will have to be revised in the light of better knowledge of the functioning of the nervous system.

The revision of all human behaviour in the light of our conclusions is beyond the scope of this book, or any one book for that matter. We will, however, treat some important particular instances fairly exhaustively.

Modern psychology is well aware of the importance of environment in the final make-up or personality, but its approach is timid and piecemeal. Some workers stress the importance of one group of conditions, some of another. Thus the Freudian school established that neuroses and psychoses are due to conflicts arising in the mind in the process of adjustment ; but psychoanalysis accepted implicitly the existing laws of society, religion and family as sacrosanct. Every individual must accept these whether he wants to or not, if he is to be normal.

The possibility of the fault being in the very conditions to which the individual is called to adjust himself might have been faintly understood but was never expressed. It was, and with many analysts still is, the rule that the patient's marital and other relations of social origin are not to be manipulated by the therapist. His job was to make the patient accept what Tom, Dick and Harry do.

However, the rapid development of analysis showed that Tom, Dick and Harry do not accept, what the patient is induced to accept, with such unreserved completeness as the layman thinks ; that neuroses of all degrees of gravity are, in fact, widespread in all layers of society ; it thus became more and more difficult to expect the patient to succeed where so many fail.

The obvious way out was to attack the immutability of the social laws, habits and traditions themselves. The attack shifted from sexual conflicts to those arising from family conditions, and at present the full weight of attack is thrown against the beliefs, traditions and economic conditions which are the foundation of our society.

Every such attack has met great antagonism, the bitterest fight being put up by the protagonists of the established school who cling to their teachings with the same tenacity as the public to their traditions.

It is hard to deny that the traditional foundations of our social structure need thorough revision. No objective observer, free of prejudice, will argue against the necessity of radical changes. Some will prefer gradual adjustment, some drastic change, but change there will be. Indeed change is ·already being effected.

In such changes lies hope for a better future. A social structure in which economic and marital conditions are devised to minimise and perhaps eliminate the greater difficulties of adjustments, should in time reduce the present increasing number of maladjustments and mental conflicts.

Yet there is no room for complacency. The fact that antagonism to revision of old notions is as strong among analysts as among laymen shows that either the analysis they undergo is not carried far enough, or that analysis cannot completely eradicate bad habits.

While expecting hopefully that the environment will be changed by our collective efforts, we must also make sure that everything amenable to human influence in each individual is used to facilitate adaptation. This will not only eliminate much misery in the present generation but will also give a better chance to the next.

In anticipation of our conclusions it may be said at once that we do tolerate certain limitations, physical and mental, just because we do not know that they are amenable to our influence. The results of faulty habits are called character or chronic diseases which, as their name suggests, are incurable. And improper use of oneself is explained as unfortunate inheritance or permanent deformation. Degeneration of the human species is so often invoked as confirmation of the futility of all endeavour to improve, that it seems proper to see what truth there is in it.

1. DEGENERATION AND IGNORANCE

ON looking closely at ourselves we may wonder why biologists have decided that we are the greatest achievement of nature, and placed us on the very top of the tree of evolution. The species just beneath us, and other immediate neighbours are, on the whole, so much better than ourselves at all vital functions that the idea of the degeneration of man is forced on many minds with great persistence ; God, or nature, has made us perfect but our original sinfulness, or man-made civilisation is at the root of all evil and imperfection. We blame civilisation, the strain of modern life, the complexity of it and so forth for the loss of many of the physiological qualities that the apes still have.

Yet there is no doubt that the biologists are right, and that man, by the development of his nervous system, is the highest of all animals. Whether this higher brain development is a consequence of greater complexity of life or the cause of it is a debatable question. The important thing is that high brain development and complexity of life go together. It is pointless, therefore, to blame any shortcoming on complexity of life. If there is anything at all in evolution theories, it is certain that complexity will go on increasing as time goes on.

It is often said that the complexity of modern life is unnatural. But in what sense is this complexity a human creation ? Thinking is assuredly a natural and properly human function. We cannot stop ourselves from thinking any more than from breathing. By going on thinking we think better and grasp things more clearly, our thought becomes richer and more complex, and so does life. We have a complex nervous system which is just as much the reason of our complexity as its product. Our nervous system enables us to make complex adaptations and, if we could stop ourselves from doing what we do, we would probably be in even greater trouble. Not to use an organ or a function is not only difficult but generally disastrous. The complexity of our life and the complexity of our nervous system are one. And our nervous system is certainly not an invention or a product of civilisation. It is just as natural for a man to write books and read them as it is natural to die or be born. In any case, we are not likely to give

9

up all the knowledge that we have acquired through thousands of years of thinking and working just to avoid complexity. Even if we did, we should only start the cycle all over again. For it is natural for a brain capable of co-ordinating speech to produce an alphabet, grammar, syntax etc. Hundreds of isolated independent human groups have travelled along the same road. This process has much more the appearance of a law of nature than an aberration of mind or folly of man.

The degeneration theory is nothing more than an admission of ignorance of how to bring about the desired changes in our mind that will satisfy our urge for happiness. And what is worse, it shows no way or direction in which improvement may be sought.

Yet there is truth in the complaint that at the present state of civilisation our shortcomings are glaring, that we are at an impasse where our achievements seem to be balanced, if not outbalanced, by a sense of frustration. We seem to know so much, yet are unable to use our knowledge to live a fuller and more satisfying life. It is important, therefore, to discover what exactly are the elements responsible for this deplorable situation ; if we knew them we might be able to control them.

It is certainly not the sense of insecurity nor the " strain of modern life," for insecurity and strain were just as prevalent, and possibly greater, in primitive life. It is difficult to compare our life with that of our stone age ancestors and draw any useful conclusions. The scales of values are totally different. The loss of wife or son to a stone age man was probably a mere trifle compared with the loss of a tool, a needle or a weapon. Life was, if anything, more strenuous then than it is today. We strike a match or switch on an electric fire—but what an effort it must have been to light a fire in primitive times, and what a strain to keep it alive. The sacredness of the fire and the shrines where fires were kept alight show how important was the fire and how great the anxiety to keep it burning. Did the man who tilled his land with a stone or a wooden plough, as it is still being tilled in some lands, have less strain than we do ? Did he feel secure without our knowledge of combating pest, without alternatives to natural irrigation ? Without modern knowledge and amenities our ancestors were subject like wild birds or silver foxes in Canada, to periodic extermination by the elements. Heavy rains flooded everything ; droughts parched everything. And there was no insurance against these disasters. Do not primitive people even today die like flies after droughts ? Imagine the composure of the primitive man when rain failed to come ! Think of the insecurity he felt when his family and domestic animals died just because of an evil eye ; and every stranger assuredly possessed one !

It would be easy to multiply examples. It is safe to conclude that neither physical strain nor actual insecurity can wholly account for our present shortcomings. It is probable that the neurotic and the hypochondriac were much more common of old than they are today.

While our social order is of course far from perfect, there is no doubt that, on the whole, life has been made easier and safer through the achievements of mankind during the scientific era. And relatively speaking, the men of whom we glibly speak as being more natural than ourselves suffered in all probability at least as much strain, anxiety and physical and mental disorder as ourselves.

Recent studies in fossil skeletons of our early ancestors show, beyond doubt, that most of the physical ailments of today were common of old. Mortality of the young was much greater than today. Dental caries were as numerous as today ; moreover, teeth were badly worn by the hard tasks to which they were put. Skeletons also prove that bone diseases, such as rickets, were very common. The number of those unfit to live at large in modern society is certainly greater than in primitive societies. The reason for this is not that the number of idiots or otherwise degenerate offspring per thousand births of *normal parentage* is now greater than before, but because we preserve piously everything that is born. We could, and some nations do, take measures to prevent the unfit reproducing ; we do not know of any means of preventing normal parents from giving birth to degenerates. There is little evidence that the genetic inheritance of healthy human stock has deteriorated.

Another argument often advanced is that the changes in modern life are so rapid that men are unable to adjust themselves to them. Our social structure is admittedly lagging behind the advancement of science, and this gives rise to certain frustration and misfitting of individuals; but here we should complain of too slow changes, rather than too rapid. What development is too rapid for men ? Does the speed of modern transport produce any ill effects ? Is there any professional disease that would not affect our ancestors in the same way that it affects us ? Does the telephone, the aeroplane make normal people into neurotics or make them flat-footed ? The sense of danger and anxiety that may come with these products of civilisation were just as common when messengers rode horses or ran. I fail to see what exactly is changing too rapidly for individuals to follow. I can rather list a whole series of radical changes that are necessary and much too slow in coming.

Before finally discarding the explanation of all our physical and mental shortcomings by the degeneration of the human race, we must see whether it is really degeneration that we mean. The biologist says degeneration when he means reversion to a lower type. Now, it is precisely the reluctance to accept lower type standards that brings to light our shortcomings. Were our conditions primitive, most of the sufferers of today would probably never have become aware of anything that would make them think that they are degenerate. We become aware of our shortcomings when we reach a more or less mature age, while genetic degeneration is congenital. Amaurotic and mongolian or other forms of idiocy are discovered in early infancy. None of these unfortunate creatures is aware of its degeneration and never strives for any higher achievements. And it is open to question, as we have already pointed out, whether the number of idiots per thousand births of normal parentage, has considerably increased in modern times. From the actual number of idiots alive at any one time we must deduct those born to idiot parents who are preserved by society's zeal to safeguard any child that is born, and who often themselves breed more extensively than the average.

In my experience the real reason underlying peoples' complaints of their state of strain, anxiety, etc., is, in every case, ignorance. Not personal ignorance, which can be remedied by asking help from those who know better, but a much worse type. I mean the fundamental ignorance that creeps into science itself ; abstractions that are generalised and temporarily exaggerated do incalculable harm. We know, in fact, very little about what life is, what is important and what is not. We needed to wait for Freud to show that a threat of castration by a loving parent may sap the vitality of the son for the rest of his life. It is hard to believe that such important happenings to ourselves, coming from the outside world, and therefore through senses and conscious perception, could remain unnoticed for so long.

Our knowledge of what is biologically important is so scanty that we worship ideas which merely sound good. For instance, we now worship an idea of extraversion with the result that even intelligent people come to think that a normal man is the one who is active, driving, enterprising all his waking life. The result is a cult of exteriorisation producing a new type of neurotics, ruining their children's lives and wasting away their own. Another scourge is the idea of concentration. So is self-control, training, conscious control and many others. Not, of course, that these are wrong ideas, but that they are taught to be absolute virtues, which they are not.

I contend that rigidity, whether physical or mental, i.e., the adherence to a principle to the utter exclusion of its opposite, is contrary to the laws of life. For rigidity in man cannot be obtained without suppressing some activity for which he has the capacity. Thus, continuous and unreserved adherence to any principle, good or bad, means suppressing some function continuously. This suppression cannot be practised with impunity for any length of time.

To my mind, the real trouble lies in the fact that we forget in the process of learning, that the principles we learn are themselves ephemeral and not absolute. That our teaching is faulty here and there is relatively of secondary importance : Specialisation in a limited range of acts for long periods is the most difficult adjustment for man to make. If a man uses his eyes as people in the past did, i.e., to look at the horizon, at the sky, at his body and at his work, the eye goes through the complete range of its capacity, and ignorance of the proper use of the eyes has no chance to cause real harm. But when the scholar, or composer, or draughtsman has to use his eyes to focus at ten inches for hours on end, day after day, it is essential for him to know how to use the eyes properly. For he puts on them an extreme demand by excluding all functioning in favour of a particular act. Some muscles, nerves and cells in the higher centres are overworked, while others must be constantly inhibited. Only a few who thus use their eyes will succeed in preserving good use of them. We often hear people say that their special incapacity is due to lack of exercise. Here we see that any training may be worse than no training at all ; for the eyes of none of these people lack exercise, yet their eyesight deteriorates steadily. The use they make of their eyes adapts them most perfectly to that particular use only, but renders them almost useless for other purposes. Thus, even a young man with perfect eyesight will not see the details that a short-sighted histologist will see in his microscope. But whereas the former will rapidly adjust himself to the microscope, the latter is unable to get normal service from his eyes in any other use. In the same manner, any strong young man with perfect feet will find it difficult to stand as long as a flat-footed liftman, for instance, or policeman, but the former can jump and run, while the latter suffers aches and pains in doing so.

The important thing, however, is the emotional disturbance that leads to faulty use of oneself. In short, it cannot be denied that greater complexity and specialisation need more perfect adjustments.

This alone is the reason why we discover in ourselves so many shortcomings. While the use we make of our faculties is far below their ultimate capacity any method of use may be good enough. But when we want the potentially best use of our faculties, our failure to obtain it is due to lack of knowledge, and not to degeneration. Had we not changed the Roman numerals and substituted the decimal system for the older ones, we would have found with the increased demand of calculation in modern life, that our mathematical capacity had degenerated. Civilisation makes it necessary to adopt better methods not only in calculation but in all other uses of self.

2. SOME PERTINENT FACTS

NERVE cells do not divide after the first year of life, many of them lose the power of proliferation long before birth. Thus, the nerve cells remain the same throughout the life of the individual. The increase in bulk is mainly due to growth of processes, the capacity for division is forever lost. The total number of cells of the nervous system is remarkably constant and does not depend on the size of the individual.

The nervous system is often divided into two : the old brain and the new brain. The new brain consists of the rind or bark of the brain, the cerebral cortex and its auxiliary structures. It has no direct connection with the muscles of the body ; they are affected by the intermediation of the old brain, i.e., the cerebellum, bulb, spinal cord; in short, all that remains of the central nervous system when the cortex and its appendages are removed. The old brain is concerned chiefly with reflex actions and message conduction to and from the cortex.

Besides the brain there is the autonomic or vegetative nervous system of ganglia lying behind the digestive tract, and this is chiefly concerned with the involuntary functions of vegetative life such as those of the ductless (endocrine) glands, the viscera, blood vessels etc.

The old brain and the new derive their names as follows : in the classification of animals, it is found that in the higher animals one part of the nervous system becomes larger and more important functionally—namely, the anterior lobes. There is also a correspondingly greater variety of activities. In man the anterior lobes are larger and more complex than in all other animals. The cortex, responsible for what we call higher activity, is therefore called the new brain, as it is supposed to have evolved subsequently to the more primitive structures of the old brain.

All the activity of the nervous system can be roughly divided into three categories : conscious activity, reflex and automatic activity, and vegetative activity. It is understood that these activities correspond respectively to the new brain, the old brain and the vegetative system.

In the course of evolution elementary nervous function is

differentiated and becomes more specialised, while the physical structure grows in bulk and complexity. Every new formation seems to be of a higher quality, assuming control over the former organisation. The functions of the newer formations are more subtle, more complex, and above all, subject to delay because of the longer circuiting and multiple relaying at the higher levels. They are therefore, in a sense, less reliable than the older formations. They also need apprenticeship and conditioning. Thus, when the irritation originating in the outside world is very sudden, intense or entirely novel, the first reaction is obtained from arc reflex structures straight away. The higher, new formations are not involved at all ; they are by-passed. As if incapable of coping with signals of too high intensity, they shunt the excitation to the cruder mechanisms that can cope more easily with such violent stimulation.

When the stimulus conveys a threat to the individual of the sort that constantly occurred to that genus, race or species for long evolutionary periods, the newer formations interfere as little as possible in the process of the reaction—not unlike an administration that cuts out some " red tape " measures in conditions of extreme emergency.

Everything occurs as if the newer formation were a tentative advancement in the nature of a biological luxury. When the threatening situation arises the response must be forthcoming at once. A crude, not quite appropriate reaction, but roughly in the right direction, and with a minimum delay, is safer than a refined, well co-ordinated and economic reaction later on. As might be expected, such reactions, originating from the more primitive and less differentiated mechanisms, are more alike in two different individuals than reactions forthcoming from more complex mechanisms having more and greater degrees of freedom. The reactions elicited from the lower structures are stereotyped on the reaction which uncounted generations have given to similar situations ; for those who reacted inappropriately have not had the opportunity to hand down the corresponding gene pattern.

Society gives up, in conditions when emergency threatens its existence, the newer, tentative forms of government, and reverts temporarily to an older form of government which acts more quickly and more expediently in the direction of group safety, but at the expense of some of its members whose immediate survival is less essential. Here, too, the older forms of government of two different societies will act with greater similarity than marked the newer tentative forms the two societies applied before the emergency.

The reversion to a more archaic pattern of behaviour is a biological expedient, because the newer forms are less certain and have no ready-made summary answer to quickly changing circumstances. The greatest advantage of the older forms of control is that they have stood the test of similar occurrences an infinite number of times in the past and will quite probably be effective once more.

Both mechanisms for switching over control to the lower structures, the higher centre cutting itself out and the higher centre being by-passed altogether, are to be found in the nervous system. In the case of very violent and sudden events it is the second alternative that is operative most of the time.

An important feature of every new formation of the nervous system is that the control it exercises on the older formations is always both excitory and inhibitory. Thus, with the advent of the new control, certain reactions will disappear. They remain alive but are suppressed so long as the newer control is operative. Others, on the contrary, will appear and be sustained permanently while the new formation is in control.

We shall see later that extirpation of certain higher nervous centres results in the appearance of an exaggerated muscular tonus which was inhibited and kept in abeyance by the extirpated centres. This excitory and inhibitory character of every newer formation in the nervous system explains many manifestations of the activity of the nervous system emerging after partial elimination of the control or its failure in the living intact organism. Partial suppression of control of different parts occurs under more or less normal conditions in everyday life, and a corresponding liberation of inhibited older activity appears or is eliminated.

The whole nervous system is found to be composed of hierarchical entities, each overriding its immediate subordinate, each in its own turn being subject to a similar influence from its superior.

John Hughlins Jackson (1834–1911) has suggested the idea of successive integrations in the evolution of the nervous system, and pointed out that in the erect posture in man, the successive higher structures are actually placed one above the other. His was an intuitive guess based on clinical observation of nervous diseases only. The work of Sherrington, Lapicque, Magnus and numerous followers substantiates this idea and gives it physiological proof.

We shall see later the importance of Jackson's law which is :
" The nerve functions that are latest to develop are the earliest to
be destroyed."

Function and not structure seems to be the best guide in forming a coherent picture of the nervous system. The layer concept
is helpful in understanding both function and structure. The whole
is essentially dynamic and fluid ; relative permanency is found
only in the lower reflex levels.

Closer scrutiny reveals many unexpected features. It becomes
clear that the whole nervous system is made in a true constitutional
fashion. It is a working structure full of compromises and " temporary " arrangements that are as permanent as any temporary
measure has ever been ; just as in the telephone service there are
out-of-date exchanges that are not scrapped but which are used
in emergencies, when the modern and elaborate circuits, that are
more liable to misfunction because of their complexity, break
down ; or as if an overcautious housewife should keep candles,
matches, a kerosene lamp, an acetylene burner, gas and electri-
city ; with the remarkable difference, however, that in the nervous system the old structures respond more quickly and more
reliably. This response is not fitting to complex situations as it
is not differentiated or subtly graded, but in vital emergencies
mostly concerned with the mechanical balancing of the body and
its rapid righting, it is elicited before the elaborate and superior
mechanisms have a chance to start at all. Moreover, these latter
generally inhibit themselves, i.e., they let the reliable and com-
petent older and lower structures act without reference to the
higher executive controls altogether.

The spreading of excitation, though nearly completely absent
in the " lines," is the rule in the relays and exchanges. The irradiation of the nervous excitation in the synapses, or relays, and
all the higher nervous centres is as absolute as the one-way conduction of the nerves. But these imperfections, from the point of
view of the electrical expert, are used to the best account possible.
Parasitic, " not intended " diffusions of excitations are often con-
verted to useful functions.

The complexity is, however, so great, that a considerable
amount of unwanted, unnecessary and quite often detrimental
activity is produced. We sneeze when looking at the sun ; tears
flow when we are grieved ; we often freeze to the spot when a
slight movement would take us out of danger ; and so on.

The irradiation of nervous excitations is greatest in the autonomic nervous system. Indeed, one may say that in the sympathetic system any impulse sets the whole system going. Stimulation of the splanchnic (the great sympathetic) nerve will irradiate even to the pupil of the eye. Compression of the eyeball slows down the heart, with some people, by up to fifty beats per minute. This is called the oculocardiac reflex which normally slows down the heart by from five to thirteen beats per minute.

The irradiation of the autonomic nervous system spreads to the rest of the nervous system. Stimulation of the central end of the vagus, for instance, abolishes the knee-jerk.

All the fibres of the central nervous system are medullated, i.e., covered with a substance called myelin. This is the insulating material of the fibres. Some physiologists, however, think that since all medullated nerves conduct faster than those that have no myelin cover, myelin participates in conduction by providing the chemical ingredients necessary for the process. The nerves of the autonomic nervous system have no myelin covering.

The nerve fibres branch only at their destination. Thus a motor cell has a long axon which ends up at a muscle. Immediately before reaching the muscle it divides into many branches, often as many as 150, each small fibre supplying a bundle of muscle fibres. In this way a muscle is under the control of only a few motor nerve cells and motor nerve fibres. For example, the soleus of a cat has 30,000 muscle fibres grouped into 230 bundles supplied by 230 nerve fibres.

The excitation of a nerve produces a contraction of all the muscles it innervates. Exciting one root only, no other muscle contracts but those that the root innervates. There is no transversal irradiation from one fibre to the next, even in the same nerve trunk, and there is no exception to this rule.

In general, a nerve cell conducts impulses in one sense only, from the dendrites towards the axon. Sherrington showed that the valve action which blocks impulses in the reverse direction is located in the synapses, i.e., in the junction between the cells, and not in the cells themselves nor in their axons. That there is no diffusion from one cell to another, axon to axon, nor any part of one cell to any part of another cell was, until recent years, considered an absolute law. However, there are cells in the sympathetic system and in the retina that have no other processes but dendrites, and cells in the olfactory bulb that are interconnected by their axons. In these cells, conduction obviously does not follow the general scheme.

The life of a cell is entirely dependent on its nucleus—it lives as long as the nucleus does and dies with the destruction thereof.

The life of a cell depends also upon its activity. Thus, after the amputation of a limb the nerve fibres degenerate slowly and this degeneration finally reaches the cell itself. It never recovers once the nucleus is altered. Generally, neighbouring cells gradually take over the function of the damaged cell to a considerable degree of perfection.

An excited cell takes a considerable time to subside to its initial state. Heat, for instance, appearing during the excitations, continues to be produced for as long as half an hour after the excitation ceases. A nerve cell continues to respond for some time to excitations, even when maintained in a medium without oxygen and any other active elements. It must therefore draw on stored up energy inside itself in chemical form. The same is true for muscular fibres. But the chemical reactions supplying the heat which appears in muscles is fairly well known, while none of the other materials found in the nerve seems to undergo any change that would account for the accompanying heat.

The excitability of the nervous tissue depends very closely on the chemical composition of the irrigating blood and the hormones present, its pH, salt content, etc.

The velocity of conduction or propagation of impulses in nerves is not the same. There are three major groups, A, B, and C, with numerous subdivisions.

The velocity of conduction in group A is from 60 to 125 metres per second ; in B, from 10 to 30 metres per second and in C, 0.2 to 0.3 metres per second.

There is a relation between the velocity of conduction and the thickness of nerves. The thicker ones, the proximal (near to the centre of the body), conduct faster than the distal thinner nerves and fibres.

The nerve fibre, like the individual muscle fibre, is excited by any stimulus above a certain minimum value. But the response does not increase with the intensity of the stimulation. The nerve, consisting of numerous fibres, responds nevertheless to intensity variation of the stimulus by more and more fibres coming into action when the intensity of the stimulus is increased.

It seems, therefore, to be quite a universal law of irritable matter that the simplest unit, be it a nervous fibre or muscular fibre, responds to stimulation—or does not respond at all, and the response is independent of the intensity of the stimulus for all values above the threshold of excitability. This minimum intensity is definite only when the unit is isolated. *In vivo* there is always an interplay of inhibition and facilitation so that the excitability of a particular element depends on the history of the adjacent elements immediately before stimulation. In general, the excitation of some cells inhibits all the adjacent ones or facilitates their subsequent excitation. Thus, rubbing the tip of the nose inhibits sneezing. It seems certain that the mechanism by which one centre influences an adjacent one is by modification of its fundamental rhythm or its excitability. We shall soon see how this is achieved.

All skeletal muscles are striated, i.e., their fibres are not smooth like the muscles of the sphincters or other involuntary muscles, but have transverse light and dark striations. The striated muscles consist of long fibres running alongside each other. They are capable of violent and powerful contractions. There are two groups of striated muscles—the red ones, contracting more slowly but for long intervals without fatigue, and the pale ones, contracting rapidly but also fatiguing quickly.

The red muscles are predominantly made of red fibres and the pale muscles mostly of pale fibres. On the whole, every muscle is a mixture of different proportions of the two sorts of fibres. The extensors have more red fibres than the flexors. The former are slower and stronger than the latter. Up to 160 fibres form a bundle to which a nerve fibre is attached. A nerve cell, its axon and the muscular fibres it supplies, make up a motor unit. It is generally accepted that a sympathetic fibre is present in each unit attaching itself to the muscle fibre at the same motor end plate as the motor nerve fibres.

Some anatomists think that the red fibres are innervated by the vegetative fibres and the pale muscle fibres by the cerebrospinal nerve fibres. In view of the relative slowness of the vegetative conduction and the slowness of contraction of the red striated fibres, this opinion finds its justification in the functional unity that is thus brought to light.

All involuntary muscles, those of the iris, the sphincters, the visceral muscles and those of the blood vessels, are all smooth, i.e., made of smooth fibres with no striation. These muscles are supplied with vegetative nervous fibres only. As already mentioned, these muscles contract slowly and fatigue slowly. The heart muscle fibre is a mixture or intermediate structure of these two kinds of fibres. It is a striated fibre but not of the same structure as the other striated muscles and is richly supplied by vegetative nerve fibres.

A whole muscle bundle containing, as already mentioned, up to 150–160 fibres, and supplied by one nerve fibre, contracts evenly, *in vivo*, though each individual fibre contracts completely or not at all ; there is no synchronic contraction of all the fibres, one fibre after another contracting in rapid succession.

The smooth muscles are fundamentally different from the striated skeletal muscles. They are, of course, innervated by the vegetative nerves. Generally the smooth muscle has a sympathetic nerve fibre and a para-sympathetic nerve fibre, the one inhibiting the action of the other.

The potential difference between the surface and the interior is measured in thousandths of a volt, and not in hundredths as in the case of the skeletal muscles. Their contraction is also much slower (tenths of a second instead of hundredths of a second), and less intense. They contract to a certain intensity (tonus) and remain so for long periods. This intensity is independent of the resistence encountered. Thus, the bladder contracts until the urine reaches a certain pressure. This pressure is the same whether the bladder is half full or overflowing. The smooth muscle is therefore said to contract plastically. It also contracts rhythmically even when deprived of its nerve supply, i.e., the rhythmic contraction is a property of the muscle tissue. The cardiac muscle has also this rhythmic property.

But the greatest difference between the smooth muscles and the striated ones is that the smooth muscle contracts with all its fibres simultaneously. Thus, if all but one nerve fibre supplying the iris muscle are severed, it will contract almost normally. And the excitation of one nerve fibre only contracts the whole muscle, and not the one bundle only, as in the skeletal muscles. The transmission is not of electrical impulses but the diffusion of a substance from the nerve to the muscle.

The gradation of contraction is obtained by variation of the quantity of secretion of substance from nerve to muscle.

We see on closer inspection that in fact there is no such sharp difference in function as the macroscopic red or pale, striated and smooth differences would lead us to think. It is almost certain that tonic contractions are performed by a different anatomical part of the muscle or by a different mechanism from that used in clonic strong and abrupt contractions.

It has been proved (Marinesco, Kreindler, etc.) that striated muscles have two chronaxies (explained later), one corresponding to high excitability usual in clonic or phasic contraction, and the other of low excitability, corresponding to tonic contraction. Microscopically, we have already mentioned that in most muscles there is a mixture of red and pale fibres. There are many theories to explain how muscles contract in two so different manners as clonic and tonic, the former fatiguing after a few contractions, the latter practically indefatigable ; the fact, however, is well established and agreed upon.

Transmission of excitation in the nerves is very slow compared with electric conduction in metals. It is of an entirely different nature ; the speed of conduction in some nerves is measured in terms of metres per second, in others of centimetres per second. Time co-ordination of any motor act can be achieved by faster conduction in longer nerves or by the excitation in long nerves starting earlier.

All transmission is attenuated on its way by the changes produced in the medium of the conductor or outside it ; so that it would be necessary to start with larger signals in longer nerves to compensate for the loss of strength which increases with distance. In nerve conduction the strength of the signal is the same all the way, and is equal at its destination to the impulse that started it. The transmission is a travelling reaction (depolarisation) which takes up some of the potential energy, locally, in the nerve, all the way. The potential energy is restored to its former level later, which takes time.

Nervous conduction is not continuous like a stream of liquid or gas, but is rather like machine-gun bullet salvos. The average number of impulses per second is, in man, of the order of fifty.

There is nothing in the nerve itself to limit conduction to one direction only. On cutting a nerve and exciting the cut ends, impulses travel along the upper branch as well as the lower branch, The valve action limiting transmission to one direction is in fact due to the synapses.

A cell may be related to some pyramidal fibres, extra pyramidal fibres, and many others. On the other hand, every fibre of the pyramidal tract, for instance, is related to quite a number of motor cells. How does a cell send impulses down one fibre at one instant and down another fibre the next, or to some of them simultaneously ? And how does the motor neuron respond to impulses from one cell one moment, and from another the next ?

We have seen that nerve fibres may be considered perfectly insulated from each other, and that there is no transversal diffusion. From Sherrington's work it is established that impulses travel from one fibre to the other in the synapses. From Lapicque we learned of the existence of constitutional chronaxies, i.e., that any excitable unit has a proper time constant and that excitations must last a given time to excite them, or have the corresponding frequency to do so. Now, if the cells adjacent to the one excited have the same chronaxie, the excitation passes to them and excites them to the same level. Isochrone cells and fibres are excited at the same time. If some adjacent cells have chronaxies only slightly different (not more than one-third) they are homochrone, and the excitation communicates only partially. The heterochrone units, i.e., those that have widely different chronaxies, remain completely unaffected. A cell responds alternately to one neighbouring cell or the other, depending on the chronaxie it possesses at the moment. There is, in fact, only one constitutional chronaxie, but a number of functional chronaxies or subordinate chronaxies, i.e. the chronaxie of any excitable unit in the living organism is not stable but subordinated to higher centres. These centres exercise their control by altering the chronaxies of the elements they excite.

Loewy, showed that if a frog's heart is perfused with Ringer's solution, and the peripheral end of the vagus nerve is excited, the perfused liquid will slow down another frog's heart. A substance found to be an ester of choline, and identified by some authors as acetyl choline, is produced. The same substance is produced when any parasympathetic fibres are excited.

The stimulation of sympathetic nerve ends causes the secretion of " sympathine " (Canon), a substance akin to adrenalin. The fibres of the sympathetic innervation near the ganglions, however, secrete acetyl choline, like the parasympathetic ones.

Other substances were found that have a pronounced and selective effect on the chronaxies of different groups of nerves. Histamine, among others, is known to be produced on stimulation of the skin.

It appears, therefore, that the vegetative nervous system produces chemical substances and regulates itself by chemical agency. We have pointed out previously that the smooth muscles which are innervated by the vegetative system contract normally even when most of the fibres of the supplying nerve are cut : a fact that could not be explained by the mechanism of conduction known to operate in the cerebro-spinal nerves supplying the striated muscles. The secretion of a chemical agent, however, explains this very satisfactorily. One fibre secreting can bring the whole muscle into contraction in the case of chemical secretion, but perhaps not so rapidly.

The relative slowness of the smooth muscles and the marked irradiation in the vegetative innervations, find their full explanation in the slower diffusion in all directions of a chemical substance as compared with conduction in cerebrospinal nerves (depolarisation).

We have seen that there are vegetative fibres in all skeletal muscles and that these have red and pale fibres. The vegetative innervation would therefore be responsible for the slower tonic contractions, and the acetyl choline and adrenalin would adjust the excitability of the musculature.

Acetyl choline has been found by many workers after stimulation at all endings of striated muscles. Dale suggested that all nerves be classified as cholinergic, and adrenergic. The cholinergic, like the parasympathetic, act by production of acetyl choline at their endings, and the adrenergic act by liberating the adrenalin-like substance we mentioned.

The action of these substances passes very quickly away as they are promptly destroyed by enzymes present in the tissues. The concentration necessary to produce contraction is minute, $1 : 10^9$ of acetyl choline produces powerful contractions.

Thus, the mechanism by which the higher centres subordinate the lower and direct messages to the proper destinations is the modification of excitability or metachronosis.

The difference of chronaxies between flexors and extensors is, in fact, due to the subordinate influence of the higher centres ; the two become isochrone or at least homochrone, i.e., of the same order if not exactly the same, when the paths to the higher centres are severed. A flexor and its antagonists may have normally, say, ten and twenty as their respective chronaxies (in a triton), which will become fourteen and fifteen on decapitation, i.e., isochrone.

For the purpose we have in view, it is superfluous to go into further details ; though the problem becomes more and more absorbing, it also becomes more and more complex. It is important, however, to add the following facts. Vegetative ramifications were identified in all cerebrospinal nerves, and the vegetative fibres are not affected when the motor plate of the cerebro-spinal nerve degenerates. Severing the vegetative innervation influences the tonus of the interested part.

To sum up, we may say that every muscle normally contracts not only to a different degree but in at least two different manners —tonic and clonic (or phasic) ; that the cerebro-spinal nerves as well as the vegetative nerves participate in any contraction. These vegetative innervations act by chemical agency, adjusting the excitability of the motor mechanisms.

The structure of the nervous system is such that it is hard to imagine purely sensory, or motor or vegetative impulses. The most abstract thought has emotional-vegetative and sensory-motor components. Abstract thinking is possible only in conjunction with a special configuration or pattern. or state of the body. The whole nervous system, therefore, participates in every act ; whether it is easily observable or not is only a matter of knowing what and how to observe.

The brain and the spinal cord are separated from their bony envelopes by membranes. Between two of them, the arachnoid and the pia, lies the cerebro-spinal fluid. The whole encephalon and spinal cord are thus immersed in this fluid from which they are separated only by the pia membrane. The cerebro-spinal fluid is similar to the lymph in its chemical composition.

The pressure of fluid and its total volume vary considerably and rapidly. Thus, on injection of a strong salt solution, water is rapidly removed by osmotic action and the brain shrinks so appreciably as to render some surgical interventions easier. The total volume of the fluid increases to keep pace with shrinkage of the brain. The pressure of the fluid is very sensitive to external stroking of the jugular veins and other external physical agents.

Speransky has shown that alternate pressure variations of the cerebro-spinal fluid has a profound influence on the entire nervous system and modifies many physiological reactions. He has built a theory of medicine on these premises, namely, that the reaction depends on the sum of irritations of the system preceding it ; the nervous system reacts as a new entity after each irritation.

The autonomic or vegetative nervous system plays an important part in regulating behaviour. The two names are rather misleading, and are today only misnomers. Physiologists used to think of the nerves and ganglia that compose them as independent of the cerebro-spinal or central nervous system. We know now that this is not so. It used to be considered that the vegetative life was entirely regulated by this system. This is not quite true either. Though it is largely concerned with the regulation of the vegetative functions, animals in which the sympathetic system has been

removed or otherwise rendered inactive survive many years (Prof.
Canon *et al., Amer. J. Physiol.* 1929. 89. 84), provided they are
not exposed to sharply varying conditions.

It is best, then, to refer to the sympathetic and parasympathetic systems, or to bear in mind the above reservations. The
importance of these reservations becomes clear when we learn that
it is now well-established that there is a sympathetic fibre in every
skeletal (striated) muscle, and a medullated fibre from the central
nervous system in the central part of every sympathetic nerve. The
independence of this system from cerebro-spinal influence, as
well as the sole responsibility for the vegetative functions are wide
generalisations of archaic interest, best forgotten.

Briefly speaking, the sympathetic system consists of two large
nerves on either side of the vertebral column and the digestive
tube.

The whole system is divided into three sections :—

(1) Sympathetic—or thoracico lumbar ⎫
(2) Parasympathetic—or cranio sacral   ⎬ efferent
(3) Afferent fibres.   ⎭

All the nerves in the first division have their roots coming out
of the thoracic and lumbar region of the spinal cord, whence
their name. All these nerves are efferent, i.e., they convey signals
from the centre to the periphery. The nerves of the second division have their roots at the upper and lower ends of the spinal
cord, and some roots higher up, in the mid-brain. Hence the
ocular, bulbar and sacral subdivisions. All these are efferent
nerves.

Finally, the third division consists of all the afferent autonomic
fibres carrying impulses from the viscera to the centre.

8. FATIGUE

THE excitability or irritability of the nervous and muscular tissue is quite different from the reaction of matter in general to a physical or chemical agent. The living nervous cell and muscular fibre recover from the reaction in a particular manner and are capable of repeating the reaction. Recovery in matter usually means dissipation of surplus energy. In the living cells, recovery is restoration of potential energy.

A living nerve and muscle fibre store energy and the irritability consists in the transformation of this energy into a travelling electric impulse in the nerve, or a contraction in the muscular fibre. The energy contained in the irritating stimulus and in the impulse is small compared with the energy involved in the reaction. When the intensity, or the duration, of the stimulus has to be considerably increased in order to produce the usual reaction, the nerve or the fibre is said to be fatigued. There are different degrees of fatigue. Normally, a time of recovery is necessary to restore the potential energy to its initial level before a second reaction can be produced. During that period, which is usually measurable in milliseconds, no response can be elicited and, generalising, one could call it fatigue. However, it is customary to apply this term to the gradually diminishing response which follows several consecutive irritations, culminating in loss of excitability.

After forty or fifty contractions a muscle will take several seconds to recover. If left to itself, it will partially recover. The recovery is hastened by the action of blood or even a salt solution. in the isolated muscle, fatigue is due to two causes :—

(a) The consumption of the substance that supplies the potential energy

and

(b) The accumulation of waste products of the same substance, due to the transformation that has taken place. Among these waste products, lactic acid is notable.

In situ, the blood stream supplies the necessary substance and oxygenates and otherwise removes the waste. If a muscle is made to contract by electrically exciting its motor nerve until fatigue sets in, and is then excited directly, it is found that the muscle, responds readily. This shows that fatigue occurs either in the nerve or its motor end plate, sooner than in the muscle. It is proved experimentally that the nerve trunk is practically indefatigable unless deprived of oxygen. The motor end plate of the nerve is therefore fatigued first.

In a living person, when a muscle is fatigued by voluntary contractions, application of electrical stimuli to the motor nerve or to the muscle itself results in powerful contractions. This shows that the fatigue is higher up in the system. In fact, the motor nerve cells responsible for the activation of the muscle are the weakest link in the circuit.

Thus, the motor nerve cell in the cortex, by failing to send the excitory stimulus, is the first cause of fatigue in muscles. The motor end plate is the next to fail. The nerve trunk is practically indefatigable.

In the end plate, the nerve arborises and its structure changes ; there is valve action here similar to that in synapses. The nerve trunk conducts either way, but the motor end plate stops any excitory state from travelling from the muscle to the nerve. Similarly, in the synapses, where impulses travel from one neuron to another, arborisation and a change of structure are elements to which the valve action is ascribed.

There is a delay in the transmission of an impulse through the end plate partly due to slower conduction in finer fibres, and partly because of energy consumption in the process. The delay is of the order of a millisecond. Thus, normally, the weakest part of the neuro-muscular chain is the end plate. It will fatigue first because impulses arrive at the end plate from many different motor nerve cells. Only in the laboratory and in the other abnormal conditions is one cell ever called on to work repeatedly alone.

In a spinal animal, i.e., a decerebrated preparation, the stimulation of a single point in the scratch area excites a scratch reflex which dies away after a few applications (four or five). On shifting the electrodes very slightly, the reflex is elicited again and can be maintained by continually shifting the electrodes on the surface of the skin. The minute shift necessary to elicit the reflex after fatigue shows that the locus of the fatigue must be in the nerve-ending. For the excitation now producing the reflex and the one that did not, are travelling to the same synapse and by the same road, except for the local nerve-ending.

In normal life, activity is never strictly confined to one and the same motor cell in the cortex.   In exceptional circumstances, when such concentration of activity is called for, there is an immediate fall of reactivity.   It is Pavlov's contention that to prevent complete exhaustion of a cell or a small group of cells on which activity is thus focused, an inhibitory process comes into being which reduces the reactivity of the cells concerned.   The spreading of this inhibitory state to the surrounding cells is what we call sleep.[1]

A clear distinction between tiredness and fatigue in the physiological sense must be made.   Fatigue is the loss of reactivity found in an anatomical unit ; tiredness is a sensation experienced by an individual which may or may not be due to fatigue of nervous tissue.

To sum up, we may say that loss of function, or faulty function is most likely to be due to overconcentrated demand on nervous mechanisms.   Activity strictly localised to a small number of motor cells will produce inhibitory phenomena and finally loss of reactivity.   Normally, however, such localisation is only possible in planned experiments or in pathological behaviour.   The peripheral mechanisms are the least liable to fatigue, and misfunction does not occur in anatomically intact units.   The source of the trouble in such cases is more central.

[1]A detailed, yet popular account of Pavlov's theory of sleep can be found in Professor Frolov's book *Pavlov and his School* (Kegan Paul & Co. Ltd.).

4. ADAPTATION AND CORRELATION

LOOKING back at the ground covered by the previous chapters, one is inclined to agree with those who maintain that all human activity will one day be explained completely by the physics and chemistry of the nervous system. A living organism may, possibly, be considered as a special transducer of chemical energy derived from ingested food. Energy is raised by the body from its degraded state to a higher potential level ; and the nervous system is instrumental in receiving, analysing and integrating signals, i.e., disturbances of small energy content reaching the sensory nerve endings, and distributing them to the executive mechanisms where large quantities of energy are thrown into activity in what is normally apparent as a response.

The relative simplicity of such a nervous system disappears when we realise that this system does not only deal passively with incoming signals, their conduction and distribution, but also with the growth and maintenance of the executive mechanisms and of itself and has some activity of its own. And once formed, the whole system is self-balancing, recovering after each disturbance to a new configuration of balance, and becomes fit again for further reaction. Many of the mechanisms of analysis, integration, subordination, conduction and vegetative organisation of the system are becoming rapidly clearer, and satisfactory explanations can be given to apparently very difficult questions that were unanswerable only a short time ago.

The approach just outlined makes it imperative that functions should have some material support as energy does not undergo any transformation from one form into another without some discontinuity in the medium in which it is manifested. A radiation, for instance, in interstellar vacuo does not change into another form of energy unless it impinges on a discontinuity of some sort.

Many abstract notions such as inhibitions, have indeed been reduced to processes in the material support of the nervous system. It may therefore be legitimate to expect that all manifestations of mental functioning, affective or abstract, will sooner or later find their material support in the physico-chemical processes from which they derive.

Life, as well as the material world, will probably never be reduced to something very simple, unless an entirely new method of thinking, not based on causality, is used.

The ultimate simplicity once thought to be achieved by the atomic theory was an illusion. The atomic theory is replaced by the nuclear theory, where more and more particles appear. There is good evidence that the particles we observe are only those that have a more or less stable existence outside the nucleus. It seems odd that there should be nothing intermediate between the electron, the positron and the nucleon, the last being about 2,000 times heavier than the others. And, in fact, a respectful array of new particles has been suggested, and some listed. It is very likely that there is a continuous process of particle formation and destruction going on in the nucleus.

Recent developments suggest that position, symmetry, configuration and pattern are fundamental elements in the structure of the physical world. These abstract notions, long believed to be human creations and having solely an aesthetic value, seem to be, to put it paradoxically, as material as matter itself.

Delbrueck's model of living matter (see Schroedinger's *What is Life ?*) presents the gene as an aperiodic crystal, again bringing to the foreground position, configuration and pattern as fundamental essential elements in the structure of reality. The common belief that a few simple elements can be found by ultimate analysis, capable of explaining all the phenomena of life, may prove to be nothing more than an oversimplification due to wishful thinking.

Recognising this situation, we can understand the comparatively recent tendency to study directly the whole instead of its parts. Numerous schools have been formed to investigate the response of the entire living frame instead of dissecting it. Synthesis takes the place of analysis.

Among those who have furthered the synthetic approach are Lloyd Morgan (*Habit and Instinct*), E. L. Thorndyke (*The Animal Intelligence*), R. Yerkes (*The Dancing Mouse*), J. Watson (*Behaviourism*), Lashley and Pavlov.

Steadily the physiologist seems to encroach on the psychologist's ground. A conflict is inevitable. It consists essentially in that the physiologists believe it possible to account for all activity by integrated reflex action on the one hand, and adjustment or conditioned reflexes on the other, never referring to the testimony of consciousness. While the psychologists recognise the physico-chemical basis of all function in the organism, but never make any use of somatic evidence, even in theoretical work. In practice, when a physical cause is discovered or only suspected, the patient is handed over to the neurologist or other appropriate specialist.

It is a difficult problem indeed. The difficulty arises mainly because fundamental simplicity is expected. The psychologist expects a psyche above material localisation, on which he can operate directly by shifting the affective content from one object to another. The tool he uses is interpretation of the material presented by the patient.

There is a common basis to all modern schools of psychology ; all believe that the adult personality is the result of adjustment of the initial urges to the surrounding conditions. The difference lies in the urge and adjustment that is stressed as the most important. For one school, it is the libido (the energy of the sexual instinct), with its oral, anal and phallic phases. For another, it is inferiority and its compensation. Other schools again stress the social influence on the formation of the personality.

We may therefore say, whatever the view we adopt, that it is universally agreed that the adult mind is the product of a certain number of genetically inherited urges which are moulded, curbed, fixed or enhanced by the environment. Bearing this in mind, it is reasonable to think that the importance attributed to one set of adjustments by one school or the other is largely arbitrary. And it is more a question of practical convenience than theoretical fundamental importance which group or set of adjustments we analyse in order to understand how well the different phases of growth of an individual have evolved, and how much rectification is necessary before the total stature of the individual will assert itself usefully and harmoniously in the prevailing conditions.

It is quite obvious that it is more important to inquire into the process of adjustment in general than into any particular set of adjustments. Such an inquiry gives each of the schools its proper place in the general scheme, and, moreover, throws open for systematic study a vast, hitherto neglected field.

An adjustment is a successful act of learning ; it is the achievement of a proper response. What is a proper response is thus the important question. Hitherto, the answer to this question has never been stated in a definite formula. The response of the average seems to be understood as being the proper response. It is a thorny and difficult question to answer, for what the average behaviour is, is left to the psychologist to decide. And this depends on the environment in which he himself matured. Everything would be perfect if the average human behaviour were the best possible. But in fact, none of the schools of psychology agrees that this position is achieved. Each finds fault in some domain of human behaviour.

An attempt to formulate what is proper in behaviour on the basis of physiological functions is made in the following chapters.

Focusing attention on the process of adjustment, rather than on any one particular adjustment, soon proves to be a fruitful approach. Not only does it bring within its scope all human activity that needs apprenticeship, but some adjustments usually thought to be of little or no importance are given their rightful place.

The successive phases of development of the libido are successive stages of learning. The adjustment of the sibling to its brothers and sisters and to the parents is also an act of learning. The fitting in with other people into a society, the attitude to work, leisure and all the other social relations, such as marriage, class, authority, etc., are all acts of learning. The posture, attitudes and facial expression are acquired features fitting the environment, and therefore come under the heading of learning. In short, any activity that has needed apprenticeship may be used to investigate the process of learning in an individual. No wonder, therefore, that the partial analysis of one or the other domain of activity has misled many to think that they thus analyse the whole personality. Similar results are obtained whether we examine the successive stages and forms of the libidinal urges, social adjustment, somatic expression of emotions, or whatever group of acquired responses we may choose, but only all of them together are a valid assessment of personality.

In support of this view it may be interesting to note that the Yogi used to, and probably still do, submit special texts for recital in different complaints. Judging by the fluency or the faults of the performance the gravity of the complaint could be assessed. The cure was achieved by teaching a correct performance. I do not know how well this method works in practice ; it is conceivable, however, that with a proper technique, interesting results might be achieved.

In general, the fact that positive results are achieved by classical psychoanalysis, by Adler's and Jung's followers and by more recent versions of psychoanalysis shows clearly that our view is, on the whole, correct.

To avoid possible misunderstanding it may be fitting to state what could be considered as self-evident, namely, that the group of adjustments on which our attention will be focused henceforward is not considered to be either more or less important than any other of the groups mentioned above. They are all complementary, though it is possible to put the accent of importance on any one group. For as Cuvier puts it (*Recherches sur les Ossements Fossils*. 2nd Edition. Vol. I. p. 16. 1821), " Every organised being forms a whole, a unique and closed system, of which all parts mutually correspond and co-operate by reciprocal reaction for the same definite end. None of these parts can change without the others changing also ; consequently each of them taken separately, represents and postulates all the others."

This so-called correlation principle which Cuvier has used masterfully in palaeontology, explains clearly why we may focus attention on a group of reactions while ignoring the rest, and still have the impression that we are dealing exhaustively with the whole being.

With a proper technique it is possible to analyse a personality solely by a study of his muscular behaviour, in the same way, and with the same results as by an analysis of his mental processes alone. Such arbitrary fragmentations of a whole, however, are bound to show limitations. In time, there is a tendency to consider the system as self-consistent and self-sufficient. The initial simplifications and assumptions in the long run are ignored, and great difficulties and confusion result from persistent forcing of experimental evidence into too narrow a frame.

By dropping the arbitrary assumption that mental processes alone are sufficient to give a full account of the personality, and by taking somatic processes into account, many difficulties are removed. In practice, two methods of attack become available, and we find some cases yielding to one and obstinately resisting the other. A judicial use of both ensures a greater number of successful treatments ; and more important still, the level to which a personality can be brought with a successful treatment is considerably higher. Re-education of the whole personality takes place ; the physical body and the mental function are attacked directly and simultaneously.

5. LEARNING—THE UNIQUENESS OF MAN

" MAN is what he is because of his brain, but I found then, that what happened since, has convinced me that my surmise was right, that a study of the evolution of posture of body gives the clue, not only to the evolution of man but that of all the higher primates." This quotation is from Sir Arthur Keith's *Man's Family Tree*. When looking for the fundamental difference between man and other animals one finds so many distinguishing features that one is at a loss to discover the most significant. Many think speech to be the most important feature ; without speech, it is said, none of the human achievements are possible. Some contend that only man has a conscious, a soul, etc. ; the definition of these latter terms is sufficiently controversial to serve as a basis for any theory. The fact is, as Sir Arthur Keith puts it, it is the nervous system of man that is different and all the rest are only clues, among which posture is one of the most illuminating. It must be understood, of course, that we are in no position to affirm that the brain is the point of departure and that the rest of the frame evolved to fit it, though there is evidence to that effect. In our ignorance of the origin of life, and being interested in behaviour, the part on which we focus our attention is the material that is capable of irritation and response. The bulk of stimuli arriving at the nervous system is from muscular activity constantly affected by gravity. Therefore posture is one of the best clues not only to evolution but also to the activity of the brain.

Most features that we consider specifically human are not exclusively so. Squirrels, bears, kangaroos and apes use their hands in almost manlike fashion. They often walk upright but none of them has the plantigrade erectness of man. There is no new quality in man but a quantitive difference and degree of development that justify the claim of uniqueness. The same is true of speech and any other observable quality.

It is noteworthy that speech, upright plantigrade carriage, sexual life and all other functions in which man differs from other animals take relatively a very long time to develop ; all such functions are quantitively so different as to amount to a new quality.

Slowness in learning to speak may seem natural. Naïvely we

36

feel that " nature " had to do its best to produce man and make a special effort to endow him with speech. No doubt this is a very satisfying thought, but what about walking ? Walking is as old as animal life, and some animals walk and leap about as soon as they are born. The foal, the calf, the kid and the lamb are remarkable examples in this respect. While man lives a good sixth of his life before sexual maturity, most of the mammals achieve this in something between a half and a third of that period or even less.

I think that the slowness of functional development in general in man, and especially in acquiring muscular control is a more fundamental feature than any particular function. Correlated with other facts this slowness of development becomes of great significance in understanding man's nature.

At birth, the human brain weighs about 300 grammes, or approximately one fifth of its ultimate weight. The weight of the brain of an anthropoid baby is sensibly the same or slightly less, somewhere between 200 and 300 grammes, but this is already about two thirds of the ultimate weight of its brain.

The average human brain weighs 1,360 grammes, but often reaches 2,000 and even, as in Cromwell, 2,231 grammes, or in Byron, 2,238 grammes. The brain of an adult gorilla, chimpanzee or orang weighs from 300 to 500 grammes.

" Man has to be sheltered and educated ; the anthropoid baby has to face the realities of life soon after birth " is the comment of Sir Arthur Keith to the above statements of facts quoted from his book *The Human Body*. This comment implies that there is a purposeful directing hand or mind behind evolution. It is less controversial and more true to facts to say that the nearer the weight of the brain at birth to that in the adult animal, the nearer the capacity for functioning at birth to that of the adult animal.

In this respect, the human baby occupies a unique position. He, of all animals, is born with the smallest fraction of the ultimate weight of the adult brain. Herein lies the most significant of all differences between man and other animals.

Animals born with a more fully grown brain come with " readymade " reactions to external stimuli, and to most stimuli they are likely to encounter in life. Their behaviour is reflective, made of complex simultaneous or consecutive reflex reactions. These reactions being inherited, ready at birth or soon afterwards, fit stimuli that were common to all previous generations. For these reasons, their behaviour is a physiological process, so long as the environment continues to be the same as that in which the reflex reaction has evolved. Should the environment change too sharply, the reflex reaction may be the doom of the species as surely as it has served it. Only if the environment changes very gradually, by minute steps, will there be gradual modification of response in the individual. A sharp, drastic change will serve as a selective differential agent for any accidental mutations in the genes of the species adding new branches to the tree of evolution.

The more mature the brain at birth the more reflective is the behaviour. Therefore, the nearer the animal brain is to maturity when born the more stereotyped will its behaviour be. There will be great similarity in movements, attitudes and reaction in general, as between one individual and another.

Learning, in the most general sense, is acquiring new responses to stimuli.[1] Thus animals being born with the ready-made responses of an almost mature brain have little capacity for learning. The acquisition of a new response is made possible only by the extinction of the inborn response. It is not impossible but extremely laborious. The rhythmical reappearance of the old response and all the other possibilities of the inborn response breaking through, follow the laws established by the school of conditioned reflexes.

Such behaviour may be said to be the result of the learning of species as a whole. And once established genetically and handed down in a mature brain, little room is left for any quick new adjustments to be made by any individual. *Had* there been an animal born with a complete adult brain, it would probably have had no facility for new adjustments at all, and its reaction would have been wholly stereotyped and predictable.

The nearer the brain at birth to its ultimate size, the more complete are the paths and circuits of the nervous system and the more ready their interconnection. This is the case with animals. They can do at birth practically everything the adult animal can do but with less vigour, precision and reliability. Nothing fundamentally different will happen in their individual life. The sexual function, which is never fully developed at birth in any mammals, will show the greatest individual variations.

But man whose adult brain is several times its weight at birth has fewer ready-made responses to external stimuli. His nervous system is growing while the external stimuli are reaching it. Environment, therefore, has a greater influence on his nervous

[1] See *Nature and Direction of Learning*, an excellent book by Professor W. H. Burton.

LEARNING—THE UNIQUENESS OF MAN 39

system than on that of any other animal. The quantitative difference is so large in this respect between man and animal, that we may consider it as a new quality.

All the higher animals produce noises. The noises are the same, whether the mammals grow among their own kin or in entire isolation. They inherit not only the muscles, nerves and urge to produce them, but the actual pattern connections, the relative strength of the different muscles etc. In man, the vocal chords and the nervous interconnections are not linked by inheritance to any particular pattern, and a child raised in complete isolation could speak to no other man. The environment and individual experience thus play a much greater part in the formation of man than of any other animal. A bird in Japan sings much the same song as a bird of the same species in Britain. That song is a genetic inheritance, an inborn activity moulded on an ancestral pattern evolved with the species.

In man there is no genetic inheritance of language, gait or any other muscular activity ; every group can make their own. Some of the similarity of muscular activity, as in speech, resembling that of the parents, must be attributed to the inherited anatomical structure which favours, in the presence of the parents, a predilection for one mode of vocal activity among many possibilities. Individual experience is thus more important in man than it is in any other animal.

The great diversity of pattern of performance by men of any act is due to this fundamental fact that the actual mode of doing in man is influenced by his experience to a degree unknown in animals. The genetic tendencies only appear as a background to the individual experience, during which the growth and formation of nervous paths and interconnections take place.

Activity during the growth of the brain influences the mechanisms concerned in quite a different and more fundamental way than is the case where the brain is fully grown. The pyramidal tract, for instance, the distinct motor tract, instrumental in association and transmission of impulses from the cortex to the skeletal muscles, is essential in all voluntary movement. Lesion of this tract suppresses voluntary movement and frees automatic lower centres. But this tract begins to form at the sixth month of foetal life and is very rudimentary at birth. The voluntary movement appears with its subsequent growth. There is, therefore, an undoubted reciprocal influence between the movements a baby is brought to perform and the formation of the tract, higher cortical centres, and executive organs. The individual experience in man is therefore of greater consequence than in animals.

How important that individual experience is remains to be ascertained by precise study. That it is more important than hitherto suspected I hope to show in the following pages.

In short, we may say that the human brain is such as to make learning, or acquisition of new responses, a normal and suitable activity. It is as if it were capable of functioning with any possible combination of nervous interconnections until individual experience forms the one that will be preferred and active. The actual pattern of doing is, therefore, essentially personal and fortuitous, and is inherently different from the genetically present pattern, and the strictly limited combinations possible in all other animals.

This great ability to form individual nervous paths and muscular patterns makes it possible for faulty functioning to be learned. The earlier the fault occurs, the more ingrained it appears, and is. Faulty behaviour will appear in the executive motor mechanisms which will seem later, when the nervous system has grown fitted to the undesirable motility, to be inherent in the person and unalterable. It will remain largely so unless the nervous paths producing the undesirable pattern of motility are undone and reshuffled into a better configuration

We can now understand how " the life history of the individual is somehow written into the cortex,[1] even in the excitable motor cortex, where functional patterns are relatively stable." The motor cortex patterns are formed in man while the paths are formed and the cell processes grow and are subject to environmental influence to a degree unknown in the rest of the animal world.

[1] See *Personality and Brain Lesions*, by Stanley Cobb.

6. CONDITIONED REFLEXES AND HABITS

WE have defined learning as the acquisition of new responses. And we have seen that for man acquisition of new responses is so much easier than for other animals, that we thought it the greatest single factor of distinction. The nervous system is enclosed in the body and comes into contact with the world outside it through the senses. However, some effects of the outer world reach the nervous system from within the body too. The effect of gravity is sensed through a continuous stream of impulses arising from the weight of the segments of the body and from matter ingested through the mouth and the nose. If irritations were never recurring, but continually new, it is difficult to see how regulated functioning could be secured. Functioning of a living organism presupposes, therefore, a certain regularity, or law, in the outside world. A deeper insight into functioning can be achieved if it is borne in mind that the executive mechanisms are always the same. A muscle can only contract and this is the only result, in essence, of whatever irritation reaches the nervous system from outside the envelope, or from inside. The contraction is its only reaction to an infinite variety of impulses arriving at the muscle from a large number of sources in all possible combinations of origin and quantity. To be explicit, it should be said that the muscle is also capable of relaxation, i.e., a reduction of its state of contraction below the level of the tonus at which it is habitually maintained.

With these elements, the organism adjusts itself to the continually changing environment. The impulses arriving at the central nervous system from the sense organs, the motor mechanisms and the vegetative system at every instant are, in consequence, constantly changing. Because of the laws governing the physical world, any one total pattern of impulses arriving at a given instant, differs only slightly from the one present at the immediate next instant. Even when the impulses arriving through all the senses change sharply, they represent only a fraction of the total number of impulses reaching the higher centres of the nervous system at that moment.

This situation is of extreme importance for the understanding of the process of learning and adaptation.

Pavlov has discovered that the total situation is reinstated at the reappearance of the signal-difference. He proved that this is happening in all cases of involuntary innervation. Thus, the inborn reaction to food being placed in the mouth, which produces a change of state of almost every element of the body, when accompanied by any stimulus he chose, could, after a certain number of repetitions, be produced by the chosen stimulus alone. He thus proved that in the involuntary innervations, at least, the total situation tends to reinstate itself with the presentation of a part of it.

It is well known that he chose salivary secretion among all the changes that occur in the total reaction to the introduction of food into the mouth. V. Bechterev has shown that conditioned reflexes can also be formed with defence reactions of the voluntary muscles.

Pavlov's work on conditioned reflexes is of great importance to the understanding of the process of learning in its most general application. It must, however, be observed that the use of the word reflex throughout Pavlov's writings is quite personal, and is much more generic than the reflex defined in every text book of physiology. Pavlov introduced the concept of acquired, tempoary connections to the cortex analysers and basal ganglia formed by external excitations. If the use of the terms in the sense Pavlov attributed to them is justified, psychology becomes at once only a translation of the conditioned reflexes theory into usual language, and loses any justification for independence. At the best, it becomes a rather loose application to voluntary innervation of findings strictly only applicable. to involuntary innervations. Pavlov and his school confidently assert that their findings are, in fact, the foundation of a new psychology based on physiological functioning. It is therefore important to see clearly that this assertion is not proved unless physiological terms are stretched beyond their accepted meaning.

In fact, Pavlov has investigated the mechanism of the acquisition of new responses in artificial laboratory conditions, i.e., he studied some aspects of the process of learning in animals. We have seen that learning in man has a greater biological significance than in animals and Pavlov's findings are therefore of the greatest importance to us, but cannot be simply extended to apply to human behaviour because the nervous system of man is, in respect of learning, a more perfect and a more varied instrument. These observations do not diminish the importance of Pavlov's work or its validity, but are useful in understanding the ground on which criticism of the physiological explanation of psychic life is based.

Let us review briefly the main points of Pavlov's findings. If a normally indifferent agent, such as any sound, light, heat, scratch or electrical effect is produced immediately *before* food is introduced into the mouth of a dog, it is found, with a certain number of repetitions of the procedure, that saliva production starts at the application of the agent without the help of the food. Thus, an indifferent stimulus, when associated a certain number of times with another that normally elicits an inborn (unconditioned) reflex, acquires the property of eliciting the inborn reflex also when applied alone. The normally indifferent stimulus (say, sound) becomes the conditioned stimulus now producing a saliva secretion which is the unconditioned reflex response to food. The saliva secretion accompanying sound is the conditioned reflex.

The unconditioned reflexes are innate and characteristic of a whole class of animals ; they are transmitted by heredity and are independent of the experience of the individual animal. The conditioned reflexes are not inherited and depend on the surrounding conditions of each individual. They disappear more or less quickly under certain conditions. They are essentially temporary. Endless numbers of conditioned reflexes can be formed from one unconditioned reflex. Second, third and higher order conditioned reflexes can be formed. The higher the development of the nervous system, the easier and the higher is the order and the complexity of the consecutive conditionings. The inborn unconditioned reflex does not require the presence of the cortex. It is present in the decerebrated animal. Salivation, for instance, takes place even in a bulbo-spinal preparation, the rest of the brain being extirpated.

Conditioned reflexes have been established with voluntary (striated) muscles, pupil, deglutition, intestinal secretion etc. Tactile, kinaesthetic, olfactory, auditory and visual stimuli have all been used successfully as conditioned stimuli. Even time itself can be made into a conditioned stimulus. Thus, if meat is given to a dog exactly four minutes after it is shown to him, a sufficient number of times, he soon begins excreting saliva exactly four minutes after it has been shown to him, even if nothing is given to him at the end of the expected interval.

In order to form a conditioned reflex, it is essential that :—

(*a*) In the initial stages, at least, the conditioned stimulus should be well defined and without ambiguous parasitic additions.

(*b*) The new neutral stimulus should be applied shortly before the unconditioned one.

(*c*) The cortex of the animal must be intact.

The rate of establishing a conditioned reflex and its intensity depends on the state of the animal and the frequency and intensity of the neutral stimulus. Normally, about thirty to fifty repetitions are sufficient to establish a conditioned reflex within a couple of days. The establishment of the reflex is indicated by a sharp fall in the interval between the application of the neutral stimulus and the appearance of the unconditioned reflex. In the case of salivation the interval will be some fifteen seconds in the beginning, falling sharply to two seconds. If the experiment is discontinued before the establishment is complete, the effect slowly fades away. At the next attempt, say a month later, only a few drops, if any, will appear. But once a conditioned reflex is established, a definite salivation is obtained at the first trial many months later.

At the beginning of establishing a conditioned reflex, the animal salivates to no special quality of the stimulus. Thus, if the stimulus is sound, he will start salivating at any sound. This is called *generalisation*. Equally, if the stimulus is tactile, the animal will respond to the application being made over a large area and at the symmetrical points. Later, *differentiation* takes place and specificity appears. The amount of salivation becomes significantly greater when the specific sound is made or the exact spot is touched.

If the specific sound is repeated for a number of times without food following, the salivation goes on diminishing rapidly. The conditional reflex disappears or is being *extinguished*.

When two reflexes are conditional, say, to sound and a black disc, if the two conditioned stimuli are applied simultaneously, the number of drops of saliva will be the sum of those obtained by each of the stimuli separately. This is called *summation*. If a conditioned reflex is established for a well defined area of the skin, say, then stimulation of nearby points produces saliva, but the number of drops decreases the further the stimulus is applied from the conditioned area. This is called *irradiation*.

If, after a conditioned reflex has been established, the animal is left alone for a few months, the reflex *decays* or weakens. A few applications will, however, restore it to its full strength or *reinforce* it.

There is lastly the phenomenon of *linking*. If, say, a conditioned reflex has been established to a particular whistle and then a gong is sounded together with the whistle only a few times ; and if subsequently the gong alone is sounded, the number of drops is considerably greater than would be warranted by the number of times the gong was used were it not associated with the whistle. This is the phenomenon of *linking*.

All the above laws of conditioned reflexes are sometimes called laws of positive conditioned reflexes, as opposed to the laws of negative conditioned reflexes which are the laws of *inhibition* or suppression of established conditioned reflexes.

External inhibition

If an unexpected extra stimulus, such as flashing a bright light, for instance, is made just after the usual conditioned stimulus, the extra stimulus has a marked depressing effect on the number of drops of saliva and the rate of their appearance. The number may drop to about one tenth of the normal. If this extra stimulus is henceforth regularly applied, its effect decreases rapidly, and on the eighth or tenth application its effect is nil. As the unexpected stimulus may be auditory, visual, tactile, kinaesthetic, olfactory etc., it is easy to understand that in order to obtain consistent results in all experiments on conditioned reflexes, a highly artificial environment must be provided in which all possible stimuli are under perfect control.

Internal Inhibition

At the beginning of conditioning, the animal responds to no well-defined quality of the stimulus. Thus, the sound stimulus may be of any frequency. When the conditioned reflex is well established, the animal will respond to the precise sound of, say, 256 cycles per second and not to 247 or 264 c.p.s. It is said that the animal has learned to inhibit its response to all other sound but the correct stimulus—within the discriminating power of its auditory apparatus.

Inhibition by Extinction

A dog with a firmly established conditioned reflex is subject to frequent applications of the conditioned stimulus alone. There comes a moment when no salivation occurs. It reappears when the unconditioned stimulus is applied once again. Also, if the conditioned stimulus is of abnormally high intensity no salivation occurs.

Conditioned Inhibition

If, say, a luminous stimulus is used simultaneously with an auditory one previously established, soon both become equally effective ; then the auditory stimulus becomes indifferent. The simultaneous application of the two stimuli now becomes equally ineffective. Only the luminous signal continues to produce salivation. It is said that the second stimulus has inhibited the first.

Effect of External Stimuli on Internal Inhibition

We know that an extra stimulus of an unexpected nature applied immediately before or after a well established conditioned stimulus produces inhibition. If a third (unexpected) stimulus is applied *just before* the inhibiting one, the result is quite surprising. The salivation is as strong as when the original conditioned reflex was applied alone. The third stimulus removes the inhibition of the second stimulus.

Generalised Internal Inhibition

Before dealing with this phenomenon it is necessary to acquaint ourselves with *delayed* and *trace* reflexes. The sound stimulus and food-giving can be done simultaneously. In this case, the conditioned reflex is called *simultaneous*. If the food is given a few seconds later, the reflex is called *delayed*. If a long time, say, several minutes, is allowed to elapse before the food is given, the established reflex is called *trace reflex*. Delayed reflexes take longer to establish than simultaneous ones, and trace reflexes longer than the delayed ; their stability decreases with increasing difficulty of establishment.

If food is given *before* the conditioned stimulus is applied, nothing happens at all unless the interval is very short indeed.

Now if the stimulus alone of a trace reflex is frequently applied, salivation decreases gradually and stops altogether. The dog becomes drowsy in the lengthy intervals. Sleep, after Pavlov, is a generalised internal inhibition. Inhibitions just like the positive reflexes, are initially vague, diffuse or generalised. Discrimination sets in later.

Induction

Suppose a conditioned reflex to 256 c/s has been well established. If a 256 c/s note is now applied immediately after a quite indifferent stimulus, say an 80 c/s note, salivation is markedly increased. It is, however, essential that the conditioned stimulus is followed as closely as possible by the indifferent stimulus. If a few seconds are allowed between the two, salivation is decreased and slower than normal. Also, the stronger the indifferent stimulus, the greater is the increase of salivation.

Induction can also be negative.

Where does inhibition occur? The following experiment is instructive in this connection. A conditioned reflex is established for a definite area of the skin. This is now inhibited by a loud noise. So that the two stimuli together mean " no food." The same area is now used for establishing a reflex other than salivation, say, the contraction of a muscle. The first time that the loud noise is applied simultaneously with the stimulation of the skin, the muscle is inhibited. This shows that inhibition is the result of association in the cortex areas, and not in the paths leading there, which are different for the two cases.

In fact, the removal of the cerebral cortex produces complete inability to form conditioned reflexes. If, however, the area corresponding to one sense only is extirpated, not all the effects connected with this sense are lost. Probably the sub-cortical mechanisms are involved in this case. Very roughly, Pavlov's theory is as follows : The subcortical ganglia are concerned with the unconditioned reflexes or instincts. This is the seat of the emotions to neurologists. Above the subcortical ganglia is the centre of the conditioned, essentially acquired and temporary reflexes. The connections between the different analysers in the cortex are loose, and are made through the activity of the receptor organs, much in the manner of experimental conditioning. The external world known through the senses is projected on to the mosaic of analysers. The cortex is a network of independent analysers.

Thus, the sound stimulus excites a cortical analyser ; if the subcortical ganglia connected with food and causing salivation are excited at the same time, a nervous connection is established between the two. Repetitions stabilise this connection so that the sound now sets the arc going without the unconditioned stimulus.

Generalisation of a reflex is due to the excitation of a large area of the cortex, i.e., irradiation. When the excitation is strong, a number of analysers of the region are excited. This is called induction. The repetition of the conditioned and unconditioned stimulus lessens the excitation around the cortical receptor.

Further away, the cortex is less excitable still, i.e., a zone of inhibition exists. It is this play of excitation spreading from the excited centre into the neighbourhood while the surrounding non-excited zone tends to extinguish the excited centre, that produces all the above phenomena of induction, inhibition, etc.

A. Lenz touched the palm of a subject a few times, ordering him to turn his hand each time. After a few repetitions, the subject turned his hand upon his palm being touched only and no order following it. This simple experiment is important. The procedure is similar to conditioning a reflex. But there is no question of any unconditioned instinctive or reflex stimulus. The psychologists would see in the experiment the mechanism of mental association. This illustrates the observation we made in the beginning of this chapter, namely, that Pavlov's work has proved, for the involuntary innervations, that the part tends to reinstate the total situation, and that psychologists knew this to be the case for voluntary innervations. It is therefore correct to say that in all sensory-motor-vegetative functioning, the whole situation is reinstated in certain conditions at the appearance of any part of it.

This conclusion will be used later to explain re-instatement of anxiety at the accidental appearance of any part of the whole situation. Obviously, that part may be motor, vegetative or sensory. We can often trace consciously the onset of a sensation, but more often we cannot find any reason at all. In those cases, it is elicited by a motor and/or a vegetative part of the total situation.

Paul Schilder, citing F. Mattauschek, says : " The patient had a severe epileptic attack in the course of a quarrel with his sweetheart. They separated. Some time later he met her by chance and had his second epileptic attack. Several months later he saw a lady in a restaurant whom he at first *erroneously* took for his sweetheart, and he had his third epileptic attack."

Similarly, habitual muscular patterns and attitudes of the body do reinstate the total situation. In such cases, and they are frequent, the subject knows no clue in the sensory sphere, in the present, that could account for the appearance of anxiety.

When a dog is conditioned to a very stringent differentiation, such as distinguishing an ellipse slightly differing from a circle, the conditioning is difficult and very unstable. Moreover, it lasts only a couple of weeks and disappears, carrying away with it all previous differentiation the dog may have learned. The dog is no more the quiet animal it was before, but is constantly struggling and howling.

When the problem presented by the sensory experience is ambiguous, that is, when it is difficult to perceive a definite difference one way or the other, disorderly action takes place instead of no action. In this disorderly activity, the opposite of what is wanted is alternately produced.

The mosaic of cortical analysers is of extreme finesse ; the analysers are independent of one another—some may be excited, others inhibited. Normally, around each centre of excitation and inhibition, there are zones of diminishing intensity. On the dividing line between two such areas the cells undergo oscillatory inhibition and excitation.

When a novel excitation or pattern is presented, a whole area of analysers is excited, and for that reason no clear differentiation can be obtained. In the beginning of conditioning, salivation will occur to any noise grossly of the same character. This is the generalised phase, corresponding to a diffuse excitation of a large number of analysers. Later a central point of excitation is differentiated and response is obtained to a definite note and no other. Thus, around the zone of excitation there is a zone of inhibition spreading and inhibiting all the cells except those responding to a precise localised excitation. There is rhythmic spreading of activity from one zone to another and back. With repetition, the intensity of oscillation abates, and there is a precise focus of excitation. This does not occur in the case of ambiguous contradictory stimuli—hence the alternating excitement and disorderly activity of the dog subjected to the stringent and difficult task of differentiating an ellipse quasi-indistinguishable from a circle.

In lower animals we find seemingly rational acts performed reflectively and we ascribe them to purposeful drives or instincts. When the environment is sufficiently different from the normal all these seemingly rational and purposeful acts become not only useless but often achieve the exact opposite of the purpose that we glibly imagine to be the active power behind them. Many animals will take poisonous food in artificial conditions, moths will burn themselves to death, birds kill themselves at lighthouses, etc.

The purpose behind the reflective acts is a product of our imagination. What we observe is that an animal and its environment are well fitted reflectively to each other, much better than the same animal and a drastically different environment.

In the human being, in whom learning is so much more essential than in any other animal before he can satisfy even his most elementary needs for survival such as food, self-preservation and the like, the environment plays even a greater part than in animals. The human society influences the child to a degree that makes complete severance from it equivalent to complete destruction.

Society gradually teaches the child, through personal contact with the adult, a series of responses which will become in time more or less automatic. These are habits of feeding, language, habits of thought and general behaviour. The difference between human habits and animal reflective behaviour is that habits only tend to repeat themselves whereas reflexes do so by definition.

The human nervous system being especially fitted to the formation of personal patterns which are more labile than genetically inherited reflexes is also better fitted for inhibiting unwanted patterns and extinguishing them.

Though formation of habits is in some respects similar to conditioning of reflexes in animals, we find some essential differences. Gratification or its withdrawal, pleasure and pain, or reward and punishment are the main means by which both are formed. In reflex conditioning the neutral stimulus must be applied shortly before the unconditioned stimulus that creates the tension for gratification. We have seen that the time interval and the order of the two stimuli are crucial points in reflex conditioning. In the formation of habits it seems to play such a minor rôle that it escapes notice. The child may be influenced by the promise of reward or the threat of punishment when the father returns home, social failure when he grows up, impotence, doom, success and power, disease or strength or even hell or heaven after death.

I contend that the time interval is as crucial in habit formation as in conditioning of reflexes. Only those threats of punishment or promises of reward have any influence on the future behaviour of the child that have been made under sufficient emotional stress to impress the growing imagination. Without this condition both the threats and the promises flow away like water off a duck's back. Once the emotional stress has been sufficient the time interval will forever be correct for as soon as the act is reproduced or the state of tension causing it is reproduced, the punishment or reward are present, often intensified to the extreme.

Habits formed as a result of immediate reward or punishment have little to do with behaviour disorders. Those in which imagination played a prominent part from the start are the root of behaviour disorders. To acquire such importance, two conditions are necessary. The contemporary situation must contain a clue which reinstates the old total situation. Gratification of some sort sustaining the habit must be forthcoming from the environment. Both these conditions take an entirely subjective form and it is not simple to discover the clue or the gratification.

Thus, every child is taught habits of personal cleanliness and hand-washing is one of them. When this habit is inculcated without special appeal to the imagination but by some physical reward or punishment nothing very exceptional happens. But, if the imagination of a masturbating child has been impressed with the idea of filth and wickedness he may, with the other conditions satisfied, compulsively have to wash his hands with a-frequency that bears no relation to hygiene. The unfortunate person will not however wash his hands all the time, but every time there is a clue in the situation that evokes the total state, something that seems polluted or soiled to him must be seen, heard or touched, or associated with a present sensation. Thus he may have just washed his hands and then realise that somebody has used his soap or towel which are therefore soiled, and he must then start all over again.

The gratification that sustains this procedure may be at least the appraisal of his cleanliness or avoidance of an unpleasant task.

The elicited response is entirely personal and cannot be regarded as caused by the stimulus. It is a once-used pattern of doing that is brought forward at slight provocation from the outside. The reaction appears as a whole, *en bloc*, largely free from the requirement of being fitted to the stimulus that sets it going.

In animals where reflective behaviour is predominant, such improper responses can be elicited at will and repeatedly. For instance, if a wild bird is let loose in a room it darts straight into the window and, though it may be so severely punished as to lose consciousness, it will attempt to fly straight ahead time and again, always with the same result. There being no conscious control sufficient to deal with new situations, the old response to go ahead is manifesting itself *en bloc* though it is out of place.

In man, where there is hardly any instinctive behaviour, an habitual pattern of doing may be set going at the provocation of a stimulus from the outside world or from the body itself. The infinite variety of afferent impressions arriving from muscles, tendons, viscera and fluids constituting a constant source of stimuli to the higher centres of the autonomic and central nervous system make it possible for one element of the stimulus to fit sufficiently into an habitual pattern to elicit the whole pattern.

A response as complex as a human act cannot be co-ordinated by chance from its elements into an act that might have been a proper one in other circumstances. Such a response is necessarily a repetition, at least partially so, of previous experience.

We have seen in the chapter on conditioned reflexes that in both voluntary and involuntary innervations, the part tends to reinstate the whole situation. Some particular feature of the present circumstances becomes a signal because of its importance in former experience, and reinstates the whole earlier situation. To the observer, the response seems entirely unwarranted ; not so to its author. He, the author, often finds the unwanted response preferable to the rational one which he tends to exclude, because earlier experience has been painful, unsuccessful or too difficult. He cannot let himself repeat the situation without special fore-thought and wary preparedness. He facilitates the queer response to exclude the dreaded one.

In the mature individual, the conscious control selects from among the pre-existing patterns formed in earlier experience, one which is the most appropriate to the present circumstances. He may be mistaken in judging the appropriateness of the response. In each case, he will alter the response if the situation is repeated. He may even be a highly gifted personality and may discard all previously used patterns and elaborate entirely new ones. A person who finds unwanted patterns of earlier experience reinstating themselves repeatedly *in spite of his conscious control*, is behaving neurotically.

For instance, every man clears his throat, adjusts his garment or shifts on his seat occasionally with more or less awareness. A person who finds himself repeatedly performing these acts without his conscious control having the opportunity of approving or dis-approving or even in spite of his efforts to stop himself, is behaving neurotically. In him, these acts are reinstated as part of an old pattern with a strong emotional content, at the slightest provo-cation from a present stimulus of external or internal origin.

The difference between queerness, neurotic behaviour and psychoneurosis is only a matter of degree and object. When the reinstatement of earlier patterns of doing occurs in trifling, un-important acts, a person is merely queer. When it interferes with the satisfactory accomplishment of tasks and acts essential to his well-being, the person is neurotic.[1]

The habit formation mechanisms are operative in all of us ; why are we not then all neurotic ? The answer is that most of us are. " They are all a bit queer but thee and me—aye, and thee is a bit queer." Most of us stick to some infantile pattern which is so charged with emotional tension that we cannot even consider the possibility of it being wrong. Our attitudes towards the body functions, work, sex, society, pleasure, etc., are rarely rational. They are, most of the time, perpetuations of an old emotionally established pattern and indicate arrested development in one direction or another.

The mature person who is able to break up previous experience and bring to bear on the present situation only those parts that are necessary for one expedient solution of contemporary problems, enjoys also greater recovery powers. To the immature person every demand from the environment of reform and change is a crisis with which he cannot cope.

The average person avoids any serious change and vegetates in some sort of static equilibrium. There is generally a shock or crisis that is strong enough to make him lose balance. So long as he can avoid these shocks he appears in good trim. The average person becomes a neurotic in certain conditions, the neurotic will become an average person provided certain environmental conditions are satisfied.

Our aim being to further development towards mature adult behaviour we are primarily interested in the labile acquired responses which are amenable to change. The innate unalterable functions do not interest us here. Habit formation is more important to us than what we glibly call instincts. Our social environment moulds us more than any other animal, and even in animals many of the instincts that we considered inborn cannot be observed when we raise the animal in strictly controlled conditions. Thus the dog that never had meat in its mouth does not salivate on seeing or smelling meat though we often rashly take for granted that it would.

[1]Poetical, introvert, meditative people are considered by many as essentially neurotic characters. They may be so, if old unwanted patterns reinstate themselves at slight provocation from present experience and interfere with the satisfactory accomplishment of immediate tasks.

7. THE ANTIGRAVITY MECHANISMS

ALL movement and change of position originating in the body are produced by muscular pull or relaxation. The muscles are able to do work only by contracting and pulling, and this makes it necessary that a body should always consist of heavy parts that move little and lighter parts moving more extensively. For pull between masses of equal weight would move both through the same distance. The trunk is the heavy part. The pull of the muscles fixed to it and to the limbs, produces the necessary extensive movements. But the trunk by itself is normally not rigid. It consists of two smaller parts, the almost rigid thorax and the pelvis. Thus, before any significant movement can be made, it is necessary that the thorax and the pelvis should be more rigidly connected. And the stability of the whole body relative to the ground should be increased in the plane in which work is to be done. Among all the numerous possible configurations of the segments of the body in each case there is a group in which the total amount of pull in all the muscles of the body is the smallest. There is no imaginable standing position without the muscles working, except, perhaps, when balanced on the head and elbows in the Yogi head stand. In the normal standing position, the head is maintained with the orbital axis horizontal by contraction of the muscles of the neck. The centre of gravity of the head is significantly in front of the vertical passing through the articulation of the head on the atlas, and muscular pull of the nape muscles is necessary to keep it from falling forward. It is maintained in this position by a partial contraction of muscles, called tone. The distribution of the tone in the standing muscles of the whole body is automatic.

The standing, or antigravity muscles are mostly extensors (except those lifting the lower jaw), i.e., those that open the articulations. The muscles of all articulations have their opposite numbers. While the articulation is being extended, the flexor that closes it is relaxing accordingly. This oscillatory flow of contraction from one muscle to its opposite number is called antagonism, and the muscles are said to be antagonistic.

A balanced distribution of tone is therefore found in the two groups of muscles in all postures.

No part of the body can be moved without all the others being affected.

Gravitation acts without cessation and when, through external causes, or through internal failure, an attitude is interfered with, the body tends to assume its most habitual attitude reflectively, i.e., rights itself.

The antigravity function consists of four elementary functions. All the four—(1) reflex standing (2) normal tone distribution (3) attitude, and (4) reflex righting—are located in the brain stem. The same muscle may receive motor impulses from the spinal cord, the brain stem, different other centres and from the cortex. There being only one executive organ and a great number of possible combinations of motor impulses, there is an integrative action of the nervous system, insuring that only one final algebraic sum of all the incitations reaches the muscle at any given time.

Impulses affecting posture come from a number of sources :—

(1) The labyrinths with the otoliths and the semicircular canals.
(2) The proprioceptive sense organs.
(3) The exteroceptive nerve endings.
(4) The interoceptive or visceroceptive innervations.
(5) Teleceptors.

(1) *The Labyrinth*, or internal ear, consists of a bony casing containing perilymph, in which is embedded the membranous labyrinth, filled in its turn with endolymph. The bony, as well as the membranous labyrinth consist of three parts : (*a*) the vestibular apparatus consisting of two little sacs—the urticule and saccule, (*b*) the semicircular canals and (*c*) the cochlea.

Among all the ducts connecting the different membranes of the labyrinth it is of special importance to note the endolymphatic canal, running from the saccule and ventricula to the cerebral dura mater, the membrane of the brain. For there is no doubt that sudden pressure changes of cerebro-spinal fluid are transmitted to the endolymph, affecting directly the vestibular innervations, and vice versa.

(*a*) *The urticule and the saccule* have each an oval patch, the maculae acousticae. Numerous calcareous, small ending otoliths are found in the mucilage covering the hair of the maculae. The macula in the urticule is horizontal. The macular patch of the saccule is vertical. The otolithic organs are concerned with the position of the head relative to the vertical. Maximal stimulation is obtained from the otoliths when their position in space is such as to hang down from the hairs of the maculae. Magnus and de Kleyn attribute extension of the legs to maximal stimulation of otolithic organs of the utricule ; and the righting of the head and the eyes to the saccular otoliths. Rotation of the otoliths from the hanging down position decreases the stimulation to its minimum when the otoliths press vertically on the hairs of the maculae.

The otoliths react to change of position of the head relative to the vertical, and are therefore the measuring indicators of the vertical alignment of the head.

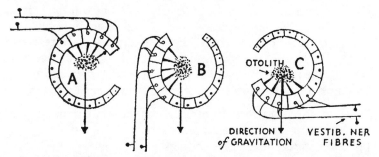

Fig. 1.—Sketch showing the influence of change of position of the head relatively to the vertical. In A the Otolith organ hangs from the hairs, in B it hangs sideways and in C it presses on them. Their stimulation decreases in this order.

(b) There are three semicircular canals in each ear. The three canals are arranged in three planes at right angles to one another. At the end of each canal there is a dilation, the ampula, in which the ends of the vestibular nerve arborise among the hair cells. The ampulae are filled with endolymph. The semicircular canals are sensitive to acceleration. As the head begins to rotate, the endolymph remains behind by inertia, and the hairs being carried by their base, are bent by the stationary liquid in the opposite sense of the rotation. The friction of the hairs against the lymph produces the impulses. When the rotation stops the liquid continues moving by inertia, and the inverse of the above happens.

When the head is rotated around a vertical axis, so that the nose moves to the left, say, the horizontal canal on the right is stimulated. The vertical canals respond to rotation each in their own plane. Tonic movements of the musculature are produced with the stimulation of the semicircular canals by rotation. When a man is rotated on a turntable, say, once a second, the following phenomena are observable. If the rotation is to the right, the eyes move slowly to the left, followed by the head. When the limit of movement of the eyes to the left is reached, they move sharply to the right and start again their slow motion to the left, and so on. This is the right horizontal nystagmus. While rotating, and especially when the rotation is over, the subject feels giddy and sick. Vertigo, nausea and nystagmus can be obtained by syringing the ear with cold water (Barany's test).

(2) *The proprioceptive sense organs* are nerve endings to be found in muscular fibres. They are excited when the muscle is elongated passively. The tendons have also nerve fibres that are excited when the tendon is pulled. The muscular receptors are called stretch receptors ; the tendon receptors are tension receptors. In general, all joints, ligaments, tendons and muscles are richly innervated. The state of mechanical tension of the different parts of the body is thus constantly projected into the higher integrating centres.

(3) *Exteroceptive nerve endings* are distributed all over the surface of the body. These are chiefly pressure sense organs. They are stimulated by contact.

(4) *Interoceptive nerve endings* are found in all the viscera. Their stimulation produces vaso motor reactions. They often produce pain and thus influence attitude. The hollow organs have stretch receptors which produce vegetative sensations.

(5) *The teleceptors* are stimulated by distant changes. The eyes, the ears and the nose are teleceptors. It is remarkable that all the teleceptors, which are double-organ devices, are close to each other, and all of them are in the head. Direction is located by means of double organs. An eye, ear or nostril, when stimulated reflectively, orients the head until the other eye, ear or nostril is equally stimulated. The position and movement of the head are therefore of great importance in our relations to the outside world. As can be expected, even from the short description above, all sensory experience is associated with movements of the head (or voluntary immobilisation of it).

Twisting, bending or rotation of the head produces direct excitation of the labyrinth which is a governing factor in the regulation of the vegetative innervation. Moreover, the endolymph is directly in communication with cerebro-spinal fluid through the endolymphatic canal. Changes of pressure of the fluid excite the vestibular nerve and vice versa. The compression of the jugular veins (the only encephalic veins) increases the pressure in the cranium.   Light stroking or touching of the jugular veins for a second or so pushes up a water pressure gauge in communication with the cerebro-spinal fluid at the lumbar level, by 5 cm. The return to normal is sharp.

A compression of the vein lasting 10 seconds will bring up the water gauge by 50 cm. in about five seconds, followed by a sharp fall. The importance of these variations is seen in the fact that normally in the lying position the gauge will read about 16 cm. (of water pressure).

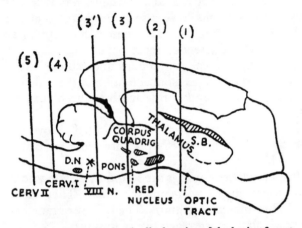

Fig. 2.—Schematic of a longitudinal section of the brain of a cat, showing different sections in connection with decerebrate rigidity. S.B. = Striated Body ; D.N. = Deiter's nucleus.

We see, therefore, that a sensory experience of teleceptor origin is, in fact, always a sensory-motor-vegetative disturbance. This is especially so in early childhood, when the sensory stimuli are new and the subject has not learned to inhibit the excitation of the whole chain of reactions in the early stages of their occurrence.

We have already mentioned the great difference between the functioning of the nervous system of man and other mammals. Several years pass before a reliable automatism of body movements is established in man ; while the calf or lamb, for example, start walking, leaping, etc., immediately after birth. The study of posture in man is complicated by the conscious control and by the importance of the optical righting reflexes. It is essential, therefore, to study the mechanisms involved first in animals. Only after this is it possible to gain an insight into the corresponding functions in man.

Among the numerous workers in this field, Rudolf Magnus and his followers, de Kleyn, Rademaker and others are outstanding. The following is a brief review of the main points.

On sectioning the brain of an animal at different levels, some of the normal functions disappear, but also certain functions become more pronounced than in the intact animal. Experience has shown that the intervals between the planes of the sections are of importance, and five different sections are normally used.

On sectioning the forebrain of an animal just behind the tractus opticus and corpus striatum, i.e., a good third of the whole mass, that which is left is called :—

(1) *the thalamus animal.* Such a preparation possesses heat regulation and normal postural reactions.

(2) *the mid-brain preparation.* This is an animal in which a section has been made lower than the previous one, but in front of the red nucleus. The thalamus has thus been removed. Such an animal has lost temperature regulation but its posture is still normal.

(3) A section made below the red nucleus causes *decerebrate rigidity*, i.e., an exaggerated contraction of the antigravity muscles.

No significant change is obtained by a section parallel to the former until removal of the vestibular nucleus. The vestibular nucleus forms an eminence on the floor of the fourth ventricule which is the terminus of the vesibular nerve. This nucleus is divided into four parts—Schwalle's nucleus, Deiter's nucleus, Bechterew's nucleus and the spinal vestibular nucleus.

(4) A section below the vestibular nucleus such as to remove the Deiter's nucleus, produces an animal in which the decerebrate rigidity disappears again but leaves the neck reflexes intact.

(5) A section of the spinal cord at the level of the second cervical produces a spinal animal in which the neck reflexes finally disappear.

It is seen that the vestibular nucleus, therefore, exercises a tonic influence on the antigravity muscles and that the red nucleus is at least one of the centres that balance this influence.

We are now in a position to follow the main points of Magnus's findings. A dead animal, when put on its feet, collapses ; so does a spinal animal. Yet a spinal animal is capable of highly perfect movements. On pinching a foot it retracts it, away from the irritating stimulus. On rubbing its skin, a normal scratching of the irritated spot is performed. If suspended in the air it " runs," i.e., moves its legs as when running. Distension of the sphincter muscle of the anus produces all the complicated movements of defæcation. But the animal cannot stand as there is no tone in the antigravity muscles.

The presence of the brain stem up to the red nucleus is necessary before the antigravity muscles, the extensors of the legs, the back, the tail and the muscles of the lower jaw, have tone. But the presence of this part of the brain only, the rest of it, including the red nucleus being removed, produces the exaggerated standing of decerebrate rigidity. The enduring tone in this case is maintained by the proprioceptive sense organs of the contracted muscles themselves.

In the thalamus animal, the tone in the extensors is just enough to maintain standing. The motor centres of the cortex have also an influence tending to decrease decerebrate rigidity, but this influence is small compared with that exerted by the red nucleus.

In a decerebrated preparation, the changing of the position of the head relative to the body evokes attitudes closely resembling normal attitudes. The changing of the head is two-fold :—

(1) The head changes its position relative to space or, more precisely, to the vertical. This stimulates the otolithic apparatus.

(2) The head is rotated, bent, and so on, twisting the neck and thus stimulating the proprioceptive organs of the deep muscles of the neck.

To separate the two influences, one has to cut the sensory roots of the neck muscles, or bandage the head firmly to the body so that no relative movement is possible. When this is done, it is found that the maximal tone is obtained in the position in which the otolithic apparatus is hanging down, and that on rotating the animal, the tone decreases to reach its minimum after a 180 degree rotation. The tone of the flexors moves in the reverse direction, though it is very weak in general.

To study the tonic neck reflexes one has to eliminate the influence of the labyrinth altogether. This means total extirpation of the labyrinth, or at least the otoliths. Destruction of the otoliths is achieved by centrifugation of the animal. Extirpation of one labyrinth or unilateral extirpation is also used.

Extirpation of one labyrinth is of special interest. It shows unerringly that the muscles involved in maintaining the body in one of the normal attitudes are practically indefatigable. For unilateral extirpation in a rabbit, results in its head being turned. This attitude will remain for ever, unless the other labyrinth is removed subsequently. The turning of the head evokes tonic neck reflexes that flex one of the forelimbs and extend the other. Muscles are the last link in the neuromuscular chain to fatigue. They will remain tonically contracted for days on end. This can be seen in catatonics, who show waxen pliability (flexibilitas cerea). Such patients maintain any position into which they are put for as long as they are left in it without showing signs of fatigue. Tonic muscular action concerned in maintaining a part of the body in unchanging positions for long periods is indefatigable so long as the tonic impulses continue to arrive. And the attitudinal tonic head reflexes seem to be practically indefatigable.

A normal rabbit, says Magnus, sits in a squatting posture, with head down, fore-limbs flexed and back curved. By flexing its head dorsally, so that the mouth is raised, a combined labyrinthine and neck reflex is evoked, by which the fore-limbs are strongly stretched, the fore part of the body raised and the back extended. The movement of the head need not be made by the hand. The result is the same if the head is raised actively by the rabbit by acting on its teleceptors.

In man, it is difficult to see simple attitudinal reflexes except in sharp, unexpected reactions, or under narcosis and when cerebral functioning is pathological. Thus, in some forms of chronic hydrocephalus, turning of the head raises the arm towards which the face is turned, and it remains raised until the head is turned in the opposite direction.

Dr. Walshe describes some cases of unilateral paralysis due to war wounds. The paralysed limb cannot, of course, be voluntarily moved ; but associated movements can be obtained when strong stimulation is applied to the healthy limb. If the head is turned towards the paralysed arm, the associated movements are extension which changes into flexion when the head is turned away from the paralysed side.

We see here two important things. First, that a muscle may be paralysed to conscious voluntary incitations while remaining active to incitations from lower reflective sources. Secondly, the lower centres take over when the inhibitive effect of the higher centres is eliminated and attitudinal reflexes become as obvious as in lower animals.

We have seen that the decerebrate animal stands. The standing is, however, precarious—a slight push and it falls. The decerebrate animal has no righting functions. The mid-brain animal, not only stands, but recovers normal standing when its standing is disturbed. The thalamus animal rights itself equally well. In both these preparations there is no voluntary function, as the fore brain is removed in both of them. The righting function is therefore purely reflective.

If a thalamus rabbit is held by the pelvis in the air so that it does not touch the ground, then, on turning the held pelvis in space, the head adjusts itself and is held continuously in the normal relation to the vertical. No matter what orientation is given to the pelvis, the head rights itself to its normal position. The righting impulses come from the otolithic apparatus, for as soon as this is extirpated, or when the otolithic membranes are centrifuged, the head does not right itself, but follows the body into the position into which it is moved by the pelvis.

Suppose the centrifuged rabbit to be held by the pelvis so that it is lying on its side, as it were. Its head is also in a lateral position. If it is now lowered in the same position, so that it touches the ground, the head immediately turns into the normal position. Thus, an asymmetric stimulation of the exteroceptive receptors on the skin rights the head. In fact, if a board is now pressed on the side facing upward, so as to equalise the pressure on both sides of the animal, the head returns to the lateral position, and touches the ground, as before. We see, here, the body-righting reflexes acting on the head as part of the general mechanism whereby labyrinthine and exteroceptive stimuli combine to bring and maintain the head in the normal position in which the otolithic stimulation is maximal.

When the head has been righted and the body held in a lateral position, the neck is twisted. The proprioceptive nerve organs in the neck muscles, joints and tendons are stimulated and the thorax rights itself so as to untwist the head. The twist is now displaced to the lumbar joints, and the pelvis is righted as well by the proprioceptive stimulation arising from the lumbar region.

We see here the neck and lumbar-righting reflexes acting so that the body stands properly and follows the movements of the head.

The righting neck reflexes acting on the body are not the only ones to influence the body. If the head is maintained in any other position than the normal one, and the body is put on to the ground, it rights itself, even though the head is maintained in the abnormal position. The body rights itself by body-righting reflexes acting on the body.

Thus the head is righted by labyrinthine and exteroceptive reflexes, while the body is righted by proprioceptive and exteroceptive reflexes. The exteroceptive stimuli are seen to control both the head and the body and bring them into the normal position. But the righting function of the head and the body have a second individual mechanism insuring proper functioning when the other mechanisms are injured or prevented from operating.

In the higher animals as well as in men there is another set of righting reflexes. While the centres of all those reflexes we have dealt with are located in the centres of the brain-stem, the optical righting reflexes are located in the cortex. In man, two visual fields overlap and one eye controls the position of the other by optical impulses, i.e., directly, without connection, say, with the tonic neck reflexes.

In a delabyrinthised monkey the righting optical reflexes are sufficient to keep the head in the normal position provided the eyes are focused on something, and of course, provided that the cortex is intact. We see here the only righting function of cortical origin which is under voluntary influence as opposed to all the others that are entirely reflective. Thus, in the higher animals there is a voluntary element involved in attitude and posture. The higher cortical centres have overriding control over other centres. In man, therefore, all the reflex standing and righting functions are masked by the cortical control.

Sherrington has pointed out the importance of the fact that most of the righting functions are located in the brain-stem, and are therefore outside voluntary control. The body tends thus automatically to bring itself into the proper position relative to gravity after it has been brought out of it by the conscious activity. This is a point of great importance. It is seen, in fact, that in animals, phasic movements are a voluntary disturbance, that is, imposed on the body, which is provided with automatic reflex mechanism for restoring to a normal posture. Only in this posture has the animal the ability of correct judgment of spatial relation in the environment, and proper control of its body in the field of gravity.

The field of gravity has acted permanently on countless generations and the same kind of movements were necessary to produce the posture in which the animal has the greatest command over its movements. The tendency towards economy in living organisms has rendered these movements automatic, independent of the higher centres except to achieve a finer degree of adjustment.

A body standing on legs has stringent conditions of balance. Some disturbances must be set right in a small fraction of a second, otherwise complete loss of balance is unavoidable. In order to be effective, the movements are stereotyped, like all reflex action, and are elicited even when the higher centres are engaged in more complex activity. Their automatism reduces failure of functioning. The lower nervous centres are also the least susceptible to damage.

However, this automatism is only useful in constantly recurring conditions, and is therefore complete only in animals with, comparatively speaking, a limited variety of movements. In the higher animals, and especially in man, the complexity of movements increases apace with the variety of conditions. Every new generation or individual may find itself in unusual conditions and the reflex stereotyped response becomes less and less useful.

The optic righting reflexes in the higher animals like cats, dogs, etc., and especially in monkeys, in which they are more important, give the animal greater freedom in movement, corresponding to the greater variety of activity. With the optical centres taking over, the cortex is given control over the lower centres, and the reference posture encountered before becomes less definite. The animal can now find its place in the picture of the environment with the eyes only. The optical impulses arrive at the cortex and voluntary, less automatic innervations are now interposed between perception and response.

In man, this trend in evolution reaches culmination. The actual innervation of the motor paths is left to grow after birth. It is as if his nervous system is left to adjust itself to the conditions in which it is likely to grow. The variety of his possible activities is now immense compared with the lower mammals, but so is also his nervous activity. There is almost none of the inherited, prototyped, ready-made response that rarely fails or is improper in its normal environment. The lability of the motor paths and the great variety of new patterns of connections in the motor centres of the cortex give rise to considerable differences in each individual in the performing of ordinary acts.

There also appears now an organism with an apparently normal anatomy, but improper functioning—a being that responds properly now and then, and fails equally often.

To sum up, in animals the head and the pelvis are oriented reflectively by gravity. The head especially tends to assume a unique relationship to the vertical—a sort of reference position with which the correct representation of space and a proper muscular response is linked.

In man, the same reflex mechanism exists, but subordinated to two more differentiated controls—the optical and conscious controls. He also needs apprenticeship of his voluntary muscles before he can bring the head into proper relationship to the vertical. The uniqueness of man in respect to learning is seen in the development of all functions in which there is a significant muscular element.

It is essential, therefore, to understand what special functions are associated with the human carriage of the head which is the only one needing such a long apprenticeship before it can assume its proper relationship to gravity.

8. ERECT POSTURE AND ACTION

THE erect posture of man is unique in the animal world. Mechanically, it is the most precarious of all known modes of locomotion. Several years pass before a sufficient degree of perfection is achieved to enable man to avail himself of all the advantages of this peculiar carriage. At first sight, it is rather difficult to see that there are any advantages at all. As far as locomotion is concerned, it seems that most herd animals are better provided for than man. Their standing is more stable. more reliable and they are able to take full advantage of it at birth or shortly afterwards.

It is often advanced that the erect carriage of man has freed his hands from the task of locomotion, and thus given him the opportunity of using them for making Man. Though the use of the hands is undoubtedly a factor of paramount importance, it is certainly not the factor that distinguishes man from other animals. For the squirrel, the kangaroo, the bear, the ape and many other animals can use their fore limbs often in strikingly human fashion, but are not notably better off than other animals. All that can be said, is that man uses his hands in a human way, i.e., we can explain how he uses them but not why. By a proper study we can find what is the way in which the hand must be used in order to yield the best result. Violinists, pianists, typists, and prestidigitators, for example, have to learn an established method of using their hands.

In the same way, studying the mechanics of the body, its anatomy and its nervous system, we can outline the advantages of the erect posture, and the use for which the body is best suited. Comparing the human body with that of other animals, we note that in man the moment of inertia of the body around the vertical axis passing through the centre of gravity is very small. It could theoretically become smaller still if the thorax were completely cylindrical.

No other animals, anthropoids included, who spontaneously adopt a more or less erect carriage, ever arrive at such a low moment of inertia per unit weight around the vertical axis as man. Perhaps we had better see briefly what the moment of inertia is, and what is its importance. When a body of mass (M) moves with a velocity (V), the energy it contains is $T = \frac{1}{2} MV^2$. To move the same mass (M) with double the velocity, we have to supply $T = \frac{1}{2}M(2V)^2 = \frac{1}{2}M \times 4V^2 = 2MV^2$, i.e., four times as much energy, and the mass will be able to do four times as much work as when moving with a velocity (V).

Suppose we screw in an eye-bolt at one end of a stick, tie a string to it and twist the string. It sets itself spinning quite readily and with little effort. Now remove the eye-bolt and fix it in the middle of the stick, again tie on the string and twist it as before. The stick will start rotating much more slowly than before, and only after numerous twists of the string. More energy is necessary to set it turning in this new position if we want it to turn with the same angular velocity, i.e., with the same number of turns per second, though the mass is exactly the same as before. It is obvious that in rotation it is not the mass that counts primarily but something characterising mass and position at the same time.

The moment of inertia ($I = MR^2$) is that quantity and plays the same rôle in rotation as mass in linear motion. The smaller the moment of inertia the smaller is the energy necessary to set the body in motion.

The moment of inertia increases very rapidly with the distance from the axis of rotation as the distance R appears in the equation as a square. Thus the moment of inertia of the average man around the vertical axis passing through his centre of gravity is about 1.2 kg. m². When rotating the same person in a horizontal position suspended on a rope tied to his belt, the moment of inertia is 17 kg. m², i.e., about fifteen times greater. Just stretching one arm forward and the other backward and standing on one leg somewhat as when skating, the moment of inertia grows to 8 kg. m², i.e., about seven times that in the normal standing position.

This very rapid change of the moment of inertia when moving our limbs away from the vertical enables us to do many of the things we could not do otherwise. The skater, for example, stretches his arms when he starts rotating, and when he has gathered speed, folds his arms sharply ; this sets him spinning even faster as he has decreased his moment of inertia but possesses all the energy he gathered previously. We can do the double and even treble somersault by suddenly drawing together head and knees by the same mechanism.

When animals adopt erect carriage on two legs, the head leans forward and is balanced by the pelvis protruding backwards, with the result that the moment of inertia of their body around the vertical axis is some four to five times what they could achieve if they adopted a true vertical alignment of the segments of the body in a man-like fashion. They become very clumsy in that position, and almost incapable of rotation, which they perform by a number of angular steps.

We have also seen the mechanisms in the body tending to bring the head, pelvis and trunk into as vertical a compilation as possible. We may therefore conclude that the human body is put to the best use mechanically when it is held in such a way as to be capable of turning itself round with the least effort, i.e., the configuration which has the least moment of inertia around the vertical axis.

It is because of this quality of the human frame that the bull-fighter, who has learned to keep very straight and fulfil this theoretical requirement perfectly, is able to stand dead still and yet get out of the way of a bull rushing at him at twenty miles an hour at the very moment he seems to be struck by the bull. He achieves this by a smooth and easy rotation.

The small moment of inertia is the result of piling up the pelvis, the trunk and the head vertically, one above the other, which at the same time brings the centre of gravity of the body to the highest possible level compatible with its structure. In this position the muscular contraction sufficient to maintain the body and prevent it from falling is the smallest possible. The minimal muscular tone is therefore present in that posture.

It is customary to begin the study of mechanics with statics, considered simpler or more elementary than dynamics. Curiously enough, in man, movement is achieved much more easily and earlier than immobility. A child begins by tumbling forward a few paces long before he can stand motionless, unsupported. Years pass before he can stand on one leg ; and many adults never achieve static perfection, so as to be able to stand for any length of time on one leg, especially with the eyes closed, though they can do all sorts of movements.

Indeed, the human body is badly suited for standing. Statues of human figures have to be strongly connected to a heavy base to prevent them from toppling over at the slightest disturbance. The head, the shoulders and trunk, all the heavy parts, are placed on top, and the base is very small in comparison with the total height. This base becomes larger in all positions in which the total height of the body is reduced—just the opposite of the requirements for static stability. A Martian visitor would not hesitate to conclude that the human body is the closest to an ideal frame designed for movement and the least suited for standing motionless.

We have seen that the reduction of the moment of inertia around the vertical axis to the smallest possible value necessitates in the human anatomy the best possible vertical alignment of the head and the trunk, and that this raises the centre of gravity as high as is compatible with the structure.

The closest analogy to the human body is a system of three pyramids with their bases uppermost, balanced on top of one another. The pelvic bone and legs form the lowest pyramid. In the middle of the horizontal base of this is the apex of the second (lumbar vertebrae), the shoulders being its base. The third inverted pyramid is the head balanced on the cervical vertebrae in the middle of the base formed by the shoulders. The next approximation is easy. Each pyramid can be thought of as a heavy mass balanced on a long light reed. We thus obtain a system of three inverted pendulums balanced on one another. This rough schematic representation is sufficient for the moment for the study of the dynamic properties of the structure. Only later will it be necessary to introduce further details corresponding to the rôle of the pelvic bone articulation with the heads (ischia) of the femoral bones of the legs.

When a system of three pendulums is so aligned that the centre of gravity of each is vertically above its resting point, the system is in equilibrium. There are three sorts of equilibrium—stable, indifferent and unstable. The stable equilibrium obtains when the centre of gravity is in the lowest possible position. In our system, the centre of gravity is as high as possible, and therefore unstable equilibrium obtains. It is this precarious unstable balance that rules all the mechanical behaviour of the human body.

Both stable and unstable balance present the following qualities or characteristics :—

(1) Easy change. Movement horizontally from the position of equilibrium in any direction involves little expenditure of energy or work.

(2) Easy to restore. Restoring equilibrium when disturbed necessitates the same small expenditure of energy as above.

(3) In the stable balance, an initial horizontal displacement cannot take place unless energy is supplied to the system. Because the potential energy is minimum, the centre of gravity being in the lowest possible position, no change of position will occur unless energy is supplied from the outside.

(4) In the unstable balance the centre of gravity is as high as possible, and the potential energy is maximum. No supply of energy from any other source is necessary to change the position. The displacement feeds itself on the stored potential energy.

When its centre of gravity is maintained at the highest possible position, the human body is fit to move in any direction with practically no expenditure of energy, and even this minimum is drawn from its potential energy. The potential energy is restored afterwards so that all movement starts from this configuration of maximum potential energy.

The standing body is thus ever ready for translation[1] movement at short notice. In that respect it is more perfect than the body of any other animal, which may be faster in one particular direction but has not the all-round freedom of movement of man.

It is in fact a general principle in the organisation of life that all mechanisms that may be called upon to function at short notice, and where the promptness of the response is essential, are all normally maintained at a configuration of maximum potential energy.

The muscular fibre, indeed every element of the motor unit, as we have seen, is thrown into action with insignificant energy expenditure, and only a minute quantity of heat appears in the contraction. All the heat, the oxygen absorption and, in short, the complete reaction which restores the potential energy to its initial value, takes place after contraction is over. The same is true of the nerve, where the bulk of the energy is involved in repolarising the nerve, and not in the depolarisation which is the active stroke.

The speed required is such that at normal temperature it would take too long to get the required movement, if the energy in every link of the mechanism had to be transformed from one form to another. The reaction in the muscles is therefore not the usual

[1]Motion in which the moving body does not rotate.

chemical reaction ; glycogen has two configurations of molecules, one involving a higher energy than the other. Normally, the higher potential energy configuration is prevalent ; the action current from the nerve starts the shifting of the molecules from the unstable high energy configuration to the stable one with lower energy content.

Only during relaxation periods do chemical reactions rewind the mechanism. This takes much longer than the action period, and only then do the quantities of heat, oxygen and CO_2 correspond with the amount of work done.

On the other hand, stable balance is maintained in all functions where constancy and not speed is essential. For, as we have seen in the stable balance, energy must be supplied to the system from the outside so that only powerful agents can upset the required balance. Moreover, the tendency is towards self-regulation as, in general, excess of energy tends towards dissipation.

The indifferent equilibrium is the one in which the centre of gravity is rigorously maintained at the same level. A cylinder lying on a horizontal plane is said to be in indifferent balance. When it is set rolling, no work at all is done against gravity. The cylinder will stop rolling after it has spent its kinetic energy in friction.

Having established the principle of maximal potential energy in the mechanical frame of the body, we must note that any deviations from that principle must be considered as inadequate ; in other words, to maintain the body in a way such that the centre of gravity is lower than it could be annuls the advantages recognised in the principle. Thus in proper walking, the centre of gravity of the human body should go up and down so slightly that it is practically maintained at the level at which it is when standing on the forward foot, with the one behind still touching the ground with the two bigger toes. Ideally, no work at all should be done in the field of gravity. The only resistance to overcome should be that of the joints which arrange themselves so as to shift the centre of gravity horizontally forward.

In the average man's gait, these conditions are far from being realised, and more work is involved than is necessary ; as in all physical bodies the loss of energy involved is accountable in the deformation of the supports and joints. There are people with excellent body mechanisms who walk in a manner fulfilling the theoretical conditions : it is difficult to describe the proper act concisely and with sufficient precision and clarity : Only example

or film projection can adequately convey the idea and procedure.

It may be said, however, that the gait satisfying the established
principle is as follows : Propulsion forward is obtained by the
upper parts of the body moving forward first, the advancing leg
propping up and stopping them from falling further down : the
ankle of the advancing leg should not therefore be advanced
further than the vertical through the centre of gravity of the trunk
at the moment the trunk comes to rest over the ankle. The other
leg lengthens by extending the ankle joint ; it does not push to
propel the body forward, but serves to direct and stabilise only.
The horizontal component forward, obtained by letting the
trunk fall, is used for propulsion. The work for moving forward is
provided by the potential energy stored in the body. The potential
level is restored by straightening the forward leg at the moment
of underpropping the body. People with proper body mechanisms
walk in this fashion. It is easy and graceful, because it involves
the least effort and labour. The grace of such walking is obtained
from the unity of action. When an act is efficient no energy is
wasted. This means also that no movement unnecessary for the
act is done. The body moves, therefore, smoothly, and describes
clear curves or lines. The aesthetic search for design and purity
in movement is thus also satisfied.

The head has its centre of gravity slightly forward of the support
on which it rests. In lowering or lifting the chin it behaves like
a lever of the first order.

Normally, the muscles at the nape must have some tonus to
prevent the head from falling, i.e., there is no position in which
the head can be balanced if the muscles of the neck are severed.

In the foetal state, the spine is flexed in one continuous curve.
In early childhood, before the child has learned to sit up and
walk, the spine is practically a straight line. Later, the pull of
the nape muscles helps to deform the cervical vertebrae, forming
a curve, the middle of which is pushed forward. The muscles of
the nape are now like the chord to the arc presented by the cervical vertebrae. The cervical spine is said to be hyperextended.
That the muscular pull plays an essential part in the curving of
the cervical spine is seen from the fact that it does not form
properly in the unfortunate cases where the baby must be maintained in plaster absolutely horizontal and motionless, and the
spine is thus prevented from bearing the weight of the head for a
long period.

Later, under the influence of the spinal extensors, the lumbar curvature of the spine forms in the same way as the cervical curve and in the same directions. The lumbar region is also said to be hyperextended. The pull upwards on the thoracic vertebrae by the neck extensors, helps to form the flexion of the thoracic region, i.e., a curvature opposite to that of the cervical and lumbar regions.

The term hyperextension is rather unfortunate. To avoid confusion we must explain it in some detail. An articulation is said to extend from a flexed position when the smaller angle between the two bones forming it increases. Most articulations are so placed that the extensors are on the posterior or dorsal side of the animal, and the flexors on the anterior or ventral plane. In man, the knee extensors and flexors only do not conform to this classification. In the standing position, most of the extensors are seen to extend the articulations against the pull of gravity. The muscle closing the lower jaw and those flexing the foot close their respective articulations against gravity, and are exceptions. They are flexor and antigravity muscles at the same time.

The cervical vertebrae have muscles on the ventral side and on the dorsal side. The dorsal muscles act most of the time against gravity and are therefore included in the extensor group. Their structure (red fibres mostly) also justifies this classification. However, in the adult, the vertebrae have such a configuration and structure that these extensors decrease the smaller angle between two vertebrae. This would happen in any articulation if the extensors could continue contracting after the articulation had been extended to a straight line. Hence the term hyperextension in the lumbar and cervical curves, in which this can be thought of as happening. Thus hyperextension, though it implies excess, describes a normal state.

The unfortunate choice made in the word becomes clear when it is found necessary to describe an abnormal exaggeration of these curves. There is nothing left to do but, say, normal hyperextension, slight hyperextension and exaggerated hyperextension ; all rather cumbersome and incorrect expressions from the point of view of directness.

The choice is unfortunate, also, because hyperextension suggests too strongly voluntary contraction, whereas in habitually exaggerated hyperextension the muscles respond poorly to voluntary directives. They are rigid, and tonically contracted. They lack the full range of contractability for phasic or clonic movements. They are short, and never relax to assume their full length, and feel string-like to palpation.

The pelvis is articulated on the femurs by ball and socket joints that are free to move in all directions. These joints alternately support the full weight of the body. The necessary rigidity is obtained in these free joints solely by muscular support. The pelvis on which the spine rests is therefore a link of major importance in locomotion. If the top of it is tilted forward, the lumbar curvature is increased and the centre of gravity is lowered. This tilting forward of the upper end of the pelvis is made possible by lengthening the extensors of the hip joints and the deep muscles of the lower abdomen. The lumbar curvature is further increased by the thorax being tilted backwards to compensate for the mass moved forward by the pelvic tilt. In order to maintain the head in its habitual relation to space, the thoracic flexion must be further increased.

The important thing is that a complex redistribution of muscular contraction is necessary to produce the tilt forward of the upper end of the pelvis or the head. This lowers the centre of gravity of the body and at the same time brings mass away from the vertical axis passing through the centre of gravity.

The moment of inertia around this axis increases very rapidly and slows down rotary movement, which moreover cannot now be performed except at a considerably greater expenditure of energy. Movement forward is also made slower and the work involved is also increased. For before one leg is freed from weight-bearing, the tilt of the pelvis must be reduced by the extensors of the hip joint, and the whole weight of the trunk lifted considerably at each step. Thus a preliminary movement is necessary before the main act of moving forward can be initiated. In an average man weighing ten stones, about five foot-pounds are now necessary as compared with half a foot-pound, the actual work involved in the horizontal translation in one step when the body is properly held.

On purely mechanical grounds it can be proved that the best way to initiate movement forward is obtained with the upper part of the pelvis leading the movement forward.

We are now in a position to appreciate the less obvious but essential functions of the erect human carriage. Compared with other mammals, it is the most dynamic posture of all. It is continuous adjustment to the ideal configuration of unstable balance.

The erect carriage is assured not by static stability but by ease of dynamic adjustment to the position of maximum potential energy. At its best, little energy is expended in these adjustments and rotation around the vertical axis is swift and easy. All directions are therefore within the normal scope of human experience, and man's activity is uniformly distributed over the entire solid angle around him.

The essential feature, however, is the minimal muscular tonus in maintaining erect posture in normal (not average) bodies. Without this, some advantages of unstable balance are not available. Functionally, stress must be laid on the dynamic character of the erect posture. Here again we are hampered by the misleading suggestions of certain words. *Ponere* and *postitura* refer to position ; a static idea is suggested therefore by the word posture. In reality, the unstable balance is essentially a dynamic state through which the entire system passes in each act as through a station where it takes its bearings and readjusts all the instruments sensitive to gravity in order to better its relation to space and improve its timing. A special pattern of nervous activity, in conjunction with a muscular configuration and a corresponding pattern of vegetative impulses, is indispensable to bring about smooth and harmonious passage of the system recurrently through this reference state.

Successful action is performed with the least exertion from this state of mind and body. Because the capacity and liberty of the frame to attempt and realise any act is greatest in this state, we will refer to it as the potent state. As no segment of the body can be moved without adjustment of all the others to a new configuration, the description of any act must necessarily be extremely cumbersome. Any act involves so many muscles and so complete an activity, that it is more useful to describe the function than the mechanism. And this is : (1) that the proper posture of the body is such that it can initiate movement in any direction with the same ease ; (2) that it can start any movement without a preliminary adjustment ; (3) that the movement is performed with the minimum of work, i.e., with the maximum of efficiency.

People with proper body control do, in fact, carry themselves in such a way that no preliminary adjustment or movement is necessary to pass from standing to walking or from walking to running. They can also reverse any undertaken movement at any time more easily than other people. All directions are accessible to their inspection while in locomotion without an intermediate preliminary adjustment.

These requirements for proper carriage are justified by the anatomy and mechanics of the body and they are valid for translation as well as rotation of the body.

The terms and form of our analysis may be novel ; not so the substance. The culture of the hip joints and posture of the pelvis have always been the central point of all esoteric teachings concerned with increasing potency, sexual and otherwise.

In all oriental languages, reduction of the exaggerated lumbar. hyperextension is synonymous with manhood. " Gird up your loins " is the Biblical expression for " get ready for a manly effort." " Sprung from one's loins " denotes fatherhood. The Yogi, the Japanese wrestler, and in fact all Orientals have always ascribed power and potency to the lumbar-sacral region.

The dependence of proper breathing on the correct holding of the pelvis was also recognised by the Yogi long ago. Many of the prescriptions for correct Asanas, when stripped of the cloud of vague and mystic symbolism surrounding them, are basically sounder than many modern schools of physical education, misusing relaxation, tonus and posture. Even keener understanding of the functions of the body is shown by Judo experts in teaching the Jigotai or defensive states and the Shizentai or the balanced upright state, synonymous with mental and physical potency. Unfortunately, only the example of the masters can convey the proper instruction, for their theory is based on and shrouded in a cloud of mystic symbolism as is all the knowledge of the Orient.

The Shizentai is essentially the potent state we have described. The graceful, precise and efficient movements executed effortlessly and without delay in any position and at any instant are made possible by maintaining the centre of gravity at the highest potential energy level possible.

The higher exponents of Judo show such great skill and perfection in the control of the head and especially the hips and lower abdomen (*Saika-Tanden*) that their performances seem to defy all laws of gravity.

Unless the pelvis and the head are carried properly, no athletic perfection can be achieved with ease, and some performances are quite impossible without these two requisites ; a fact well known to all specialists and yet generally little appreciated.

All people with well matured mind and body functions carry

themselves in the potent state. Marked deviations are found together with marked immaturity of other functions. The all-round matured individual is recognisable by his outstanding capacity for recovery from unexpected shocks or disturbances, mental, emotional or mechanical. Faulty recovery is never found on one of these planes of activity alone. This is a very important point to which we will return.

Outwardly, the potent state is observable by certain features common to all acts performed by the person. They are simple and direct. No effort is apparent no matter how difficult the exertion, nor how great the work may be. All the faculties and previous experience are smoothly co-ordinated to bear on the present circumstance, no matter how unexpected and violent the demand may be. When the emergency is over, deliberate reflection only corroborates the adequacy of the spontaneous response. The musculature shows no useless contraction in any part of the body. All the articulations participate in every act. None is held rigidly in any particular configuration not dictated by the immediate task being performed. In motion, none of the articulations retains any useless, habitually preferred configuration. In short, the whole system is integrated on the present circumstance with perfection and poise, preparing the body and mind for future acts. The instances where the frame is carried on by inertia are as short as possible and any performance can be reversed, or stopped, if the circumstance demands. Such an ideal behaviour is within the capacity of every frame in which all functions have full maturity— an extremely rare circumstance.

Perfect maturity of the antigravity function is recognisable by the narrowness of gait. The traces left by the feet when advancing fit between two parallel lines, about two-thirds of the width of both feet, apart. The two heels never touch the ground simultaneously. Prints of the bare feet on the ground would be so spaced that following points would be on one straight line—the middle of each heel and the edge of the second toe facing the big toe. The legs move simply, i.e., they do not do anything else but the movement strictly necessary for the purpose. So does the whole body. The trajectories described by each part in motion are therefore smooth curves. There are no jerky, angular movements whatsoever, except in sharp accidental righting.

The following chapters deal with the reasons of failure to achieve the perfection which should, ideally, be the average normal for all anatomically intact persons. Means whereby re-education of faulty response may be efficiently achieved are also suggested. To understand the reason and judge the soundness of these suggestions it is necessary to inquire into the relation of the vestibular apparatus and spatial representation and particularly into an antigravity attitude and its connection with anxiety.

9. SENSATION AND VESTIBULAR APPARATUS

ORIENTATION in space is an essential function for any living organism. We normally maintain a peculiar vertical alignment quite distinct from all other animals. The precarious mechanical equilibrium is made good by a complex play of muscles that keeps our constantly shifting body vertical, and as far as our awareness is concerned, practically free from gravitation.

All perception and sensation take place on a background of muscular activity. And though we are unaware of it, this activity is most strictly shaped by gravity. There are several systems cooperating in orientating our bodies, but the vestibular apparatus is the co-ordinating *chef d'orchestre*. It is more closely connected to primitive motility than vision. Reaction to auditory signals is faster (0.12 to 0.18 of a second) than to optical signals (0.19 to 0.22 of a second). The auditory centres in the cortex are much less localised than the visual ones. Auditory centres are encountered earlier in the scale of evolution. The vestibular apparatus coordinates all sensory impulses that influence muscular tone and attitudes.

There is no isolated sensory impulse. Every impression, even if artificially produced, is at least mixed with kinaesthetic sensations. We cannot perceive unless we are aware of the attitude and orientation of the body. On awakening in a strange and unaccustomed position, we fail to locate the image of the body in space. A sense of anxiety pervades us when we suddenly realise that we have no control over orientation. Until the head or at least the eyes have picked up the habitual relation to space we feel lost. Our flexors contract involuntarily and violently until a familiar muscular pattern is produced in the teleceptors' control.

We are not necessarily consciously aware of the special relation of the body to space and orientation. The vestibular apparatus takes a definite part in every single perception. It is well known that dizziness is connected with disorder of the vestibular apparatus. Pallor, nausea and vomiting, the breathing and pulse alterations occurring with them, are all connected with the excitation of the vestibular apparatus. All these reactions can readily be

79

elicited. The influence of the vestibular apparatus on the vegetative nervous system is well established.

The vestibular apparatus has also an influence on the visual
field. Almost every patient with labyrinthine disorders complains
of the darkening of the visual field. During the irrigation of the
ear, many patients see everything as through a mist. Darkening
of the visual field is generally present with labyrinthine fistulae.

Hans Hoff and Paul Schilder report a case of central vestibular
lesion, verified on autopsy, due to an accident. Twenty years
later the patient still had attacks with loss of consciousness. He
had a vertical nystagmus, facial paralysis, constant dizziness ;
objects turned round him in the frontal plane. When looking with
one eye, objects were doubled. He had marked anomalies in
postural and righting reflexes. His left arm behaved differently
when lying from when standing. He saw all objects inclined
30 degrees to the right side. Numerous similar cases are cited in
the literature on the subject. Space perceptions generally
are distorted, intersected lines become parallel, and vertical lines
are seen inclined.

Disorder of the vestibular apparatus distorts the appreciation
of size of objects ; the integration into one image of the multiple
pictures optically perceived by the eye is also upset.

Distortion of the appreciation of weight is also prevalent. In
general, the appreciation of weight is an algebraic sum of the
tonus and the sensation due to the weight stimulus. When the
eyes are closed the appreciation of equality of weight of the arms
is a function of the tonus prevalent in each arm. The following
experiment makes this clear. Stretch both arms in front of your-
self on a horizontal plane. With the eyes closed, lift, say, the right
arm at 45 degrees to the horizontal. Keep this posture for ten or
twenty seconds and then bring the lifted arm back to the horizontal plane, keeping the eyes closed all the time. Now open them,
and you will find the kinaesthetic appreciator false—the right
arm will be higher than the left. With the eyes open all the time
the preliminary lifting of one arm does not interfere with the
correctness of their horizontality.

The eyes constantly correct the appreciation of space due to
kinaesthetic incitations. Without them the horizontal and vertical
reference are a function of the tone prevalent in the body segments,
and do not coincide with the true vertical and horizontal.

In dizziness the loss of balance occurs because one side of the
body is sensed as lighter. The visual correction failing, a false

vertical is sensed and the righting towards this false vertical brings the body out of balance.

The image we make to ourselves of our body weight and size is distorted when the vestibular apparatus is subjected to sharp changes of acceleration. This is observable in the rapid accelerations and decelerations of lifts. One feels not only heavier when the lift stops going down, but also shorter. During the motion downwards, one feels lighter and longer. There is, of course, actual increase of pressure on the soles of the feet when the lift stops going downward. That the sensation of heaviness is due, at least partially, to the vestibular apparatus is obvious from the vegetative disturbance occurring in many people at the first experience of the lift.

We cannot conceive consciousness without fixing the position of our body in relation to the outside world. More precisely, we cannot appreciate any sensory experience, emotion or feeling without presenting to ourselves our relation to the vertical. On awakening, before we know " where " we are, i.e., before we resume the habitual relation to gravity or know how we could assume it, all signals coming from the outside world are blurred, distorted and meaningless. Opening the eyes gives us at once the orientation in space. But without the incitations from the vestibular apparatus the opening of the eyes is not sufficient.

After prolonged immobilisation of the vestibular apparatus, when the visual field moves there is no appreciation of weight, and everything turns. With the first movements of the head all the moving pictures at once fall into their normal relationship to the outside world.

No sensation is possible without some motor background. A change in tonus distribution pattern of some muscles, at least, takes place with every sensory experience. We must accommodate to see. Even when focusing at infinity the two visual fields must be shifted so as to overlap in a definite manner. On hearing, we swallow, to equalise the pressure inside the ear to that outside us, and we adjust the tensor tympani. We must breathe in for smelling. Only weak cutaneous impressions are imaginable without appreciable motility. It must be remembered that there is a change of attitude in general, because no sensory stimulus is absolutely indifferent to us. There are vegetative reactions to the slightest sensation. In fact, the term " sensation " is meaningless without a primitive sensory motor connection, association or memory.

In general, there is no isolated sensory experience. From the beginning there is a tendency towards testing each new sensory experience by the other senses. Things seen must be touched, tasted and smelled. Things that can only be seen, like the sun, the sky and the heavenly bodies, remain mysterious and intriguing even after a lifetime of astronomical study. This persistent tendency to test anything with all the senses possible, plays an important part in the development of sexual relations. So long as an object of attention is only seen there is a strong urge to touch it, to taste it, hear it etc.

In the appreciation of sensory experience, the vestibular apparatus, though by no means the only mechanism, is essential. For it co-ordinates the sensory motor impressions into a coherent picture with the image and orientation of our body in space. The vestibular apparatus derives its importance from the fact that it co-ordinates motility, which is at the bottom of all configurations of sensations. We can see that the notion of an isolated sensation is a purely theoretical convenience. Only with a great effort of imagination can we think, for instance, of separate optical and acoustical space. They are linked in our nervous system by a common motility of the head, and therefore feel as one. We know now that the sympathetic nervous system invades the whole soma. It has ramifications in the vessels, muscles, intestines and in the skin. The vestibular apparatus has direct influence on the vegetative nervous system.

Even from this summary review it is legitimate to say that the relation of an organism to the world is made through sets of sensory-motor-vegetative reactions. Such sets remain inseparable entities. They are conditioned together and each element possesses the power to reinstate the whole situation at which the set originally occurred. That such a quality is associated with sensory impressions is well known. We have shown that it is not legitimate to speak of a sensory impression separately from motor-vegetative changes. The whole situation may therefore be reinstated by either of the three elements of a set or total reaction. The motor part, the vegetative part or the sensory part of a situation as experienced by an individual has the power to reinstate the whole situation.

10. THE BODY PATTERN OF ANXIETY

McDougall distinguishes fourteen different instincts : parental, sex, food-seeking, fear or escape, combat, constructiveness, curiosity, repugnance, acquisitiveness, appeal (reciprocal of parental instinct), herd instinct (gregariousness), self-assertion, self-submission and laughter. Pavlov thinks that there is an instinct for freedom, that an animal objects to being tied up or enclosed in a confined space limiting its movements.

In physiology an instinct is a complex integration of inborn, unconditioned reflexes as distinct from acquired and conditioned ones. The inborn reflexes are characteristic of the central nervous system of any whole class of animals ; they are inherited and their formation is therefore utterly independent of individual experience. If we examine, say, the parental instinct, and find what is left of it after subtraction of what is definitely acquired through imitation and instruction, a nucleus is left that is empty of almost anything the word " parental " has come to mean. The notion " instinct " is used too loosely and is a source of many misconceptions.

However, even if we accept for the moment the above classification, we observe a remarkable thing—that only one of the instincts inhibits motion, namely fear or escape. An animal, when frightened, either freezes or runs away. In either case, the first reaction to the frightening stimulus is a violent contraction of all the flexor muscles, especially of the abdominal region, a halt in breathing, soon followed by a whole series of vasomotor disturbances such as accelerated pulse, sweating, up to micturition and defæcation.

The contraction of the flexors inhibits their antagonistic extensors, or antigravity muscles ; thus no displacement occurs before this initial reaction is over. An initial inhibition of the extensors goes together with all sensation accompanied by fear. This is at first sight somewhat surprising. One would expect the first reaction to be such as to withdraw the animal from danger as quickly as possible. It is not so when the frightening stimulus is too near or too violent. The violent stimulus produces a general contraction ; only, the chronaxies of the flexors are in general

83

lower than those of the extensors, and they contract first. Their initial contraction brings into operation the stretch reflex in the extensors which are thus capable of a greater effort. The initial flexor contraction, however, also enables the animal to freeze and simulate death if the danger is too near. All the other disturbances are descriptive of an increase of adrenalin content in the blood which is preparatory to possible violent effort of the heart and other muscles.

A new-born infant is practically insensitive to external stimuli. At birth he hardly reacts to light effects, to noise, smell and even moderate pinching. He reacts violently to immersion in very cold or hot water. Also if suddenly lowered, or if support is sharply withdrawn, a violent contraction of all flexors with halt of breath is observed, followed by crying, accelerated pulse and general vasomotor disturbance.

The similarity of reaction of a new-born infant to withdrawal of support, and that of fright or fear in the adult is remarkable. This reaction to falling is present at birth, i.e., inborn and independent of individual experience. It is therefore right to speak of the instinctive reaction to falling.

Charles Darwin has written a little book *The Expression of Emotion in Man and Animals*. In spite of many inaccuracies, it is a very important book. I think it will be considered in time as the first reliable work in psychology. There are more facts in these few pages about emotions as seen in the living body than in many modern treatises on psychology. The attitude of fear, the sinking of the head, the crouching, the bending of the knees, etc., etc., as described by Darwin in this book, are but details of the general contraction of all flexor muscles compatible with the act of standing.

No reaction similar to that sensed as fear by the adult can be elicited in the new-born baby, except by sharply altering its position in space. When it begins to hear better, about three weeks after birth, it will respond also to very loud noises. It is a well-known fact that stimuli stronger than usual, diffuse and irradiate in accordance with certain laws. Thus, if one hand is moderately pinched, that hand will be withdrawn reflectively. If the pinching is increased and the hand to which the stimulus is applied is prevented from moving, the opposite arm will twitch. If the stimulus becomes vigorous or violent, the legs and the whole body are brought into action.

M. A. Minkovsky has found extreme irradiation, i.e., spreading of excitation, over the whole nervous system in human embryos. On scratching the foot, for example, the whole musculature, trunk, neck and head react. In new-born infants, the spreading of excitation is also greater than in the adult.

Very loud nbises excite the cochlear branch of the VIIIth cranial or auditory nerve sufficiently to diffuse and excite the vestibular branch of the same nerve. This irradiation takes place not in the nerves, but at the first relays and possibly at higher centres still in the adult.

The VIIIth cranial nerve divides near the periphery into two branches—the cochlear, concerned with hearing, and the vestibular, concerned with equilibrium. Reference to Testut or Shaefer's anatomy would show how closely and intricately these two branches are interconnected. The diffusion of strong impulses is, of course, not limited to the VIIIth cranial nerve. Higher up, at the superior olive, strong incitations, produced by very loud noises, will diffuse and excite the Xth cranial nerve, instrumental in holding breath[1].

Strong impulses from the vestibular branch will diffuse in the same way to the superior olive, and will produce a halt of breath. The halt of breath is a sudden disturbance of the cardiac region. It is this disturbance in the diaphragmatic and cardiac regions that is sensed as anxiety. Some people describe it as a sensation of the heart falling out, or as emptyness or cold in the region immediately below the sternum.

The vestibular branch of the VIIIth cranial nerve innervates the semicircular canals and the otolithic apparatus. It is the former that senses any change in acceleration, while the otolithic apparatus senses slow movements of the head relative to the vertical.

Thus, the reaction that the adult interprets as fear of falling is inherited, inborn, and needs no personal experience before it is operative. And sudden, sharp lowering of a new-born infant elicits the whole series of reflexes which are the reaction of the body to falling. The first experience of anxiety is therefore connected with a stimulation of the vestibular branch of the VIIIth cranial nerve.

In the first fortnight or so, the baby is almost insensitive to noise. A little later, he will respond to very loud noises, which are the only ones by which he is affected. The stimulus is therefore very strong, and diffusion to the vestibular path will take place. The

[1] See Starling's *Physiology*, 8th Edition, page 30.

noise must of necessity be near the threshold of feeling and is probably also sensed as pain. The baby is startled, which also adds direct stimulation of the semicircular canals due to the jerk of the head.

The topology of the innervation of the ear is responsible for the ready association of loud noises with fear. It also explains why psychologists have generally mistaken the fear of loud noises for the first unconditioned fear. In the anthropoid and man, the fear of loud noises is of little differential selective significance. The newly born infant is so helpless that the mother carries it continuously, and had it no fear of loud noises, it would not perish more quickly in any case. Fear of loud noises is hardly an essential biological necessity in early infancy.

On the other hand, a new-born arboreal primate falling off a tree, as they probably all did in violent earthquakes, has a fair chance of survival if the thoracic cage is made resilient by a violent contraction, holding the breath with the head being flexed in the general flexor contraction. This not only prevents the head from being smashed against the ground, but also insures that the point of contact with the ground will be somewhere in the region of the lower thoracic vertebrae or in the lower region, precisely where the top of the arc is formed by the flexor contraction of the abdominal region. The shock will therefore be transformed into a tangential push along the spinal structure, on either side of the point of contact, and absorbed in the bones, ligaments and muscles, instead of being transmitted directly to the internal organs, and so injuring the body fatally. It is permissible to think that this is a selective differential factor, and that infants who did not produce such a reaction to falling had smaller chance of reproduction. The surviving species has therefore this precise inborn reaction to falling.

It may be interesting to note that in the reaction to falling, as I describe it, support is given to Sir Arthur Keith's view that " it was on the trees, not on the ground, that man came by the initial stages of his posture and carriage."[1]

The attitude of the body taught in Judo to break falling is exactly the same as that elicited in the baby by the stimulus of falling. Teachers of Judo may therefore find in the above description the explanation of the difficulty of beginners to use their arms to break the fall. The arms tend to flex in accordance with the inborn reaction to falling. Beginners, therefore, tend to hurt

[1] See his *Man's Family Tree*.

their elbows before they learn to control and inhibit consciously
the flexion of the arms. Later they learn to flap the ground, i.e.,
completely dissociate movement of the arms from the instinctive
pattern of flexor contraction elicited by falling. Falling on the
back with the head and abdominal flexors contracted enables the
body to withstand a fall from a considerable height with impunity.

The baby's crying is also more understandable when it is
part of the reaction to falling, rather than to loud noises. The
fallen baby is in need of immediate protection and feels pain.
The crying following the stimulus of a loud noise not diffusing to
the vestibular path is, in general, superfluous, since the mother
supposedly knows at least as well as the baby its significance and
the information of danger it may convey.

The reflective gripping of any object introduced into the hand
of a new-born baby during the first few weeks is probably another
aspect of the flexor contraction and its importance in infancy.
Observing young apes clinging to the hairy chest of their mother
is strongly suggestive.

To sum up, the inborn fear is that of falling. The anatomical
structure makes it imperative that the next fear that can be sensed
is that of loud noises. The unconditioned sensation of anxiety is
elicited by stimulation of the vestibular branch of the VIIIth
cranial nerve. All other fears and sensations of the anxiety syn-
drome are therefore conditioned. The basic pattern of all fear
and anxiety is the irritation of the VIIIth cranial nerve through
one of its branches at least. The fear of loud noises is not inherited
and not instinctive. In all normal infants, however, that reflex
will be the first conditioned one because of the similarity of their
anatomy.

Fear and anxiety are here seen to be the sensation of impulses
arriving at the central nervous system from the organs and viscera.
We shall see later that there is ground for considering all emotions
as excitations arising from the vegetative or autonomic nervous
system and the organs, muscles, etc., that it innervates. The arrival
of such impulses to the higher centres of the central nervous
system is sensed as emotion.

We have already mentioned Freud's contention that anxiety
is the central problem of neuroses. Paul Schilder[1] finds dizziness
to occupy a similar position. I quote :—" Dysfunction of the
vestibular apparatus is very often the expression of two conflicting
psychic tendencies ; dizziness occurs, therefore, in almost every

[1] See *Mind, Perception and Thought* (Columbia), page 134.

neurosis. The neurosis may produce organic changes in the vestibular sphere. Dizziness is a danger signal in the sphere of the ego, and occurs when the ego cannot exercise its synthetic function in the senses, but it also occurs when conflicting motor and attitudinal impulses in connection with desires and strivings can no longer be united. Dizziness is as important from the psychoanalytic point of view as anxiety. The vestibular apparatus is an organ, the function of which is directed against the isolation of the diverse functions of the body."

It may be interesting at this point to cite Paul Schilder's following passage, reflecting an almost kindred approach to our subject :—
" We would expect that such a sensory organ, receiving only half-conscious impressions and leading to a motility of an instinctual and primitive type, would be very sensitive to emotions and would therefore play an important part in neuroses and psychoses. It will react strongly, and we may even expect that changes in the psyche will immediately express themselves in vestibular sensation and in tonus. Organic changes in the vestibular apparatus will be reflected in the psyche structures. They will not only influence the tone, the vegetative system, and the attitudes of the body, but they must also change our whole perceptive apparatus and even our consciousness.

" These general considerations make it possible that the study of the vestibular apparatus may have great importance for the understanding of psychotic and neurotic states."[1]

Having traced the physiological source and basis of anxiety, new avenues are opened for improving; and in certain cases changing, the treatment of neuroses. Anxiety, in whatever form it may be present, must have been formed by successive conditioning from the unconditioned series of reflexes that constitute the inborn response to falling. Any treatment may therefore be considered as aiming at the extinction of a conditioned response and the formation of a more desirable one in its place. The recidive character of anxiety may thus be explained by the incompleteness of psychiatric treatment that leaves all the somatic links and facilitated nervous paths untouched. The extinction of the conditioned reflexes is therefore never complete. With interruption of treatment, the muscular habitus being left unaltered, the old conditioned response will gradually be re-established, or reinforced, to put it technically.

However important this problem may be, our aim is a much

---

[1] *loc. cit.*, page 85.

wider one. We have seen that the fear of falling elicits the first
inhibition of the antigravity muscles, and that anxiety is associated
with this process. On examining even the most generous list of
instincts, no other one but fear is found which inhibits motion.
Now, the problem of " can " and " cannot " is fundamentally
a question of doing, i.e., muscular activity. Even doing nothing
involves muscular activity of great complexity. We may therefore
expect to throw a new light on all phenomena accompanied by
chronic or habitual muscular contraction. A closer study of the
nervous mechanism concerned with equilibrium is therefore
necessary. It is worth while, however, to examine more closely
the ground covered, and answer some questions that arise in connection with it.

An interesting question may be asked : Why does an attacking
animal roar or otherwise give up the great advantage of un-
detected approach to its prey ? The advantage of producing a
sudden loud noise is two-fold. First, sudden loud noise produced
nearby elicits the response to falling, i.e., a violent contraction of
the flexors, thus momentarily inhibiting the extensors. This nails
the attacked animal to its place for a short instant, giving the
attacker a better chance by enabling it to pounce on a fixed target
instead of a fleeing one. Natural laws do not favour one species or
the other, and the strong contraction of the flexors is conducive to
an ulterior much enhanced contraction of the extensors. For the
longer the state of inhibition and the stronger the stretching of the
extensors, the stronger will be the following outburst of contraction
due to nervous induction and the stretch reflex. The attacker and
the prey both derive an advantage. Normal conditions of equilibrium between the respective numbers of the preying species and
the preyed upon are obtained by other factors. This equilibrium
is, by the way, continuously shifting with a periodicity given by
the climatic cycles.

The second advantage of roaring, is the effect it has on the
animal doing so. The expulsion of air from the lungs in roaring
is conducive to vigorous muscular contraction, and abates
excitation. Men, too, find it easier to produce a great physical
heave by expelling air and producing a deep sound such as
" heh " or " hah " at the same time.

That the excitation of one point of the nervous system, when
strong enough or when repeated at close enough intervals, diffuses
and radiates to neighbouring centres, is a well-established fact.
Darwin, in his *The Expression of the Emotions in Man and Animals*,

gives a number of examples.   To quote one from page 80 of
the " Thinker's Library " edition :—" As soon as some primor-
dial form became semi-terrestrial in its habits it was liable to get
dust particles into the eyes ; if these were not washed out they
would cause much irritation of nerve force to adjoining nerve
cells, the lachrymal glands would be stimulated to secretion.   As
this would often recur and as nerve-force readily passes along
accustomed channels, a slight irritation would ultimately suffice
to cause a free secretion of tears.

" As soon as by this, or by some other means, a reflex action of
this nature had been established and rendered easy, other stimu-
lants applied to the surface of the eye—such as cold wind, in-
flammatory action, or a blow on the eyelids—would cause a
copious secretion of tears.   The glands are also excited into action
through the irritation of adjoining parts.   Thus when the nostrils
are irritated by pungent vapours, though the eyelids may be kept
firmly closed, tears are copiously secreted ;   and this likewise
follows from a blow on the nose.   A stinging switch on the face
produces the same effect.   In these latter cases the secretion of tears
is an incidental result, and of no direct service.   As all these parts
of the face, including the lachrymal glands, are supplied with
branches of the same nerve, namely the fifth, it is intelligible that
the effects of the excitement of one branch should be spread to the
other branches."

The explanations of why we sneeze when looking at the sun,
why we cry when we are grieved, and many other facts, are on the
same lines.   Translated into modern terms of conditioning of
reflexes the above quotation is very similar to the line of thought
I have followed.

We have seen that in the infant, before its hearing is differential,
i.e., before it can distinguish between different noises, only loud
noise elicits a response, which is the same as to the stimulus of
falling.   In the adult, who has learned to inhibit this response to
most loud noises of habitual occurrence, it can still be observed
with unexpected very loud ones.

" Auditory reflexes . . .   According to the strength of the
stimulus there may be blinking of the eyes only, or, if the sound is
loud, blinking and holding of breath.   If stronger still, in addition
to the above, all movements temporarily cease, and for a very
loud sound indeed the limbs may become toneless and the body
may fall."[1]

Starling's *Physiology*, 8th Edition, page 303.

Professor Bekessy[1] has proved that loud noises produce eddies in the semicircular canals in such a direction as to make the head tilt reflectively towards the source of noise. He reproduced the phenomena on his model ear.

Thus it may be considered as established that the excitation of the cochlear branch of the auditory nerve irradiates and produces a response as if the vestibular nerve has been excited. Irradiations are governed by the configuration of the synapses and their valve action. It is therefore interesting to know whether excitation of the vestibular branch produces any auditory response. It seems to inhibit audition momentarily while the excitation lasts. If one falls or slips abruptly while being spoken to one has only a vague impression of noise during the period while the righting reflexes operate.

We have seen that any anxiety complex established through a series of successive conditionings must have started from the in-born reactions to falling sensed through the vestibular branch of the auditory nerve. That the excitation of this branch is followed by a succession of disturbances : contraction of flexors, halt of breath, accelerated pulse, sweating, blushing and even micturition or defæcation. How many of the enumerated responses will actually be apparent depends on the intensity, duration and suddenness of the initial stimulus. An increased tonus of the flexors, halt of breath and quickening of pulse accompany even the slightest excitation. Most of the time, the colour of the face changes and perspiration takes place, though they may be so slight as to be perceptible only to the acute observer. The subject, however, is aware of them consciously, and has in general learned to control and inhibit their completeness.

Because of habit of thought we cannot help seeing a reason and purpose in evolution as if it were the product of some intelligence like our own. In fact, we can find innumerable reasons for every reflex with every new point of view. If we examine the reflective closing of the eyes when an intense light is thrown on them we can see that the immediate effect is to shut off the intense stimulus from the retina. Next, the eyes are maintained at a level of low light intensity and the pupils accommodate by dilating so that on reopening the eyes they are capable of distinguishing objects at normal light intensity. Without the shutting of the eye-lids, the pupils would remain contracted and a longer time would elapse before the eye could see normally. In every reflex we can

[1] See *Hearing*, by Stevens and Davies.

distinguish the same phases—the immediate reaction that undoes the effect of the stimulus or reduces it, and the after effect which, in general, tends to eliminate the disturbance the reaction has produced in the organism, and to restore it to its original state.

The stimulus of falling similarly produces a disturbance which brings into operation all the righting reflexes. The important point to note here is that the sensation of fear and anxiety due to the disturbance of the diaphragmatic and cardiac region are actually abated by maintained general flexor contraction, and in particular that of the abdominal region.

The falling body contracts its flexors to preserve the head from hitting the ground and to strengthen the spine by arching it. In the adult, the same response lowers his head, makes him crouch, bends his knees and halts his breath. His limbs are thus drawn nearer to the body in front of the soft, unprotected parts—the testicles, the throat and the viscera. This attitude gives the best protection possible and instils a sense of safety. The flexor contractions, when maintained, are instrumental in restoring the normal, undisturbed state.

The incitations arriving at the central nervous system from the viscera and muscles in this crouched attitude are synonymous with safety, quietening of the pulse and restoration of normal breathing. All the large articulations being flexed, the resistance to the circulation is largely increased and the pulse slowed down. The cardiac muscle must, however, be capable of the extra effort necessary to contract the heart against the suddenly increased resistance and the higher pressure in it. This was, in fact, assured by the additional adrenalin content in the blood resulting from the initial stimulus.

This pattern of flexor contraction is reinstated every time the individual reverts to passive protection of himself when lacking the means, or doubting his power, of active resistance. The extensors or antigravity muscles are perforce partially inhibited. According to my own observation, all individuals classified as introvert have some habitual extensor rigidity. Either the head or the hip joints are therefore leaning abnormally forward ; turning the body is achieved by detour or roundabout means and not in the simplest direct way. Extroverts on the other hand have a more erect standing posture and gait.

In general, every pattern of impulses reaching the central nervous system from the viscera, muscles and soma in general is associated with an emotional state. The muscular contraction being voluntarily controllable, creates a feeling of power and of control over sensations and emotions. This is in fact so. To every emotional state corresponds a personal conditioned pattern of muscular contraction without which it has no existence.

Many people know that they can control in themselves physiological processes, such as preventing a headache from taking hold of them, and many other similar sensations, but dare not say so for fear of being thought ridiculous. Others, on the other hand, have elaborated this process into a theory of control of the mind over the body. All these people, introvert and extrovert, proceed by controlling the contraction of voluntary muscles. They form certain individual patterns which are conditioned with the sense of well-being. In their case, it is mostly to prevent the reinstatement of the anxiety pattern.

We can now understand how exaggerated hyperextension of the cervical and lumbar curves becomes habitual. It is rare to see young children with the head improperly balanced. There is less voluntary interference with muscular control and the head is balanced reflectively in all alike, except for anatomical structure differences. Repeated emotional upheavals condition the child to adopt an attitude which brings a sense of safety and enables him to abate anxiety. We have seen that such passive safety is brought about by flexor contraction and extensor inhibition. Voluntary directives inhibiting the extensors are therefore observed in all emotionally disturbed persons. In the long run, this becomes habitual and remains unnoticed. The whole character is, however, affected. The partially inhibited extensors become weak, the hip joint flexes and the head leans forward.

The pattern of reflective erect standing is disrupted. Conflicting directives are issued from the nervous system. The lower antigravity mechanisms tend to bring the body into the potent state. Habitual conditioning tends to bring about the pattern of rest, of safety. Conscious awareness now sides with one and then with the other tendency. The antigravity mechanisms are at work without break. Like all fatigued nervous functions, they are initially overactive ; hence the tonic contraction and string-like texture of the antigravity extensors. The overriding conscious control, however, prevents reflective erect standing. Hypnotise, or otherwise relax the conscious control, and erect standing at once improves to the extent the anatomical deformation of inter-articulation surfaces will permit. It is essential in this context to make a clear distinction between awareness and the conscious or voluntary as opposed to the reflective.

People in the unfortunate situation described live on an intellectual level. All their body functions are interfered with by voluntary directives. Conscious control, when properly directed, often improves certain details here and there, but intellect is no substitute for vitality. A sense of futility of life, tiredness and a wish to give it all up is the result of overtaxing the conscious control with the tasks the reflective nervous activity is better fitted to perform. The conscious control is paramount in integrating all the functions fitting the immediate circumstances. The internal mechanisms enabling him to succeed, should be left to the self-regulating nervous co-ordination. At least, in the present state of our knowledge of the nervous system, we can do no better than follow the best adjusted and mature specimens, and they do not abuse the conscious control.

11. MOTILITY AND ADJUSTMENT

ALL movement, whatever its purpose may be, like closing the eyes when remembering or thinking, is, in the last analysis, an anti-gravity action. Not only is the ocular globe moved as a mass in the field of gravitation, but the rest of the body is set in a special attitude and is thus maintained against the tendency of gravitation to bring it down. There is little awareness of all this constant adjustment to very stringent requirements, but the nervous system is constantly and without break, responsive to gravitation, so long as there is any life in it. Therefore, when we speak of antigravity function, we refer to motility in general.

The importance of the gravitation function, anatomically and from a mechanical point of view, has been raised in our exposition to such pre-eminence that one would expect very serious consequences in all cases where the adaptation to gravity is not perfect. Yet not only are persons with perfect body mechanics rare, but we often see individuals with very poor body mechanisms apparently successful and content.

The situation is similar to that shown by psychoanalysis. Here, too, persons with perfect libido history and development are rare, yet we see many apparently happy individuals afflicted with all sorts of complexes.

There are two main reasons for this apparent discrepancy between theory and practice.

(a) The unique freedom in man for making personal muscular patterns for all acts.

(b) Tradition and habit.

The act of sitting, for instance, may be learned to become so conditioned to the chair that the Japanese and Bedouin modes of sitting, without the use of appliances or furniture, become impossible altogether. I know an example a of well-known scientist who could not sit in the Japanese style after four years' repeated trials twice a week. And this in spite of the fact that in early childhood children do sit quite spontaneously in the same fashion all over the world without any sitting implement.

95

The unique facility of learning in man is responsible not only for the great divergence of manner in the most elementary acts, unknown in any other species, even among individuals of different continents, but it also explains how it is possible to do and think quite improperly and yet feel right. There being no instinctive mode of doing in most acts, we can learn any performance. The improper mode, however, needs conscious attention and has always elements of indirectness in it ; the " roundabout " approach to the simplest problem is the outstanding feature of inferior learning. Such learning tends to reinstate situations in their minutest details which acquire an exaggerated importance, often greater than the act itself. In habitual acts and situations, it is always possible to learn to achieve a goal, no matter how unsatisfactory the mode of doing may be from a more general point of view ; one has time to think and get ready ; also, habitual circumstances are rarely of crucial importance, so that no immediate bad consequences are noticeable. In suddenly changing conditions, the fault becomes glaringly obvious, just as emotional maladjustment shows up in sharp traumatic events.

The second reason is mainly founded on ignorance. Most people are prone to find faults in their body and behaviour, but do not know what to do about correcting the situation. Later, when grown up, most people give up the idea of basic change in themselves. The idea that faulty behaviour is a personal misfortune often leads to the conclusion that it must be covered up. The result is that the majority present outwardly a veneer designed to cover up all shortcomings.

From early childhood, they receive confirmation that this is the right thing to do. They see their parents changing their comportment, dress and general behaviour when they go out. They see their teachers do the same thing when a person of authority visits the school. They are actually given guidance to learn this covering up of inadequate posture and behaviour, instead of being helped to learn the proper way.

There are some fortunate children who are given constructive guidance, or are left alone ; the majority, however, receive instruction of an affective character only. It is " do " or " don't " with no guidance how to comply with these instructions. More often than not, the child is already aware of what is wanted, but cannot do it. It is wrong to order a child to sit up. If he does not do so himself, he has already been thrown out of proper development, and something must be done to make him feel right only in the proper posture. Goading or punishment only distort the emotional pattern, and force the child to cover up the symptom which is the cause of his troubles. He is not improving, but hiding his faults. He soon learns to put on a suit of character when not alone, to hide the real self.

Most people actually change their habitual posture on leaving home, when being observed or when unexpectedly confronted with a person whose relation to them is of interest. Obviously, they are aware of their normal inadequacy. Everybody works out his personal pattern of holding breath, of stiffening here and there—smartening up, it is called—contracting his mouth or brows ; in fact, every part of his body that he believes may convey an idea of his personality. This method of covering up instead of perfecting, being the result of ignorance, succeeds only superficially. Even though ingenious persons may develop this masquerade business to an astonishing degree of perfection, and waste real gifts on futile procedure, they sooner or later come to feel a sense of emptiness and futility, and many lose interest in life.

The neurotic achieves an outward appearance of well-being by a consciously adopted presentation of himself which, however, rarely misleads the specialist's eye. The inadequate adjustment to gravity is also masked in the same way, but it is much more difficult to disguise this inadequacy than any other. For the veneer consists of a conscious muscular effort supplementing the usual one. This is always directly noticeable, especially if the subject is unaware that he is observed. It is particularly evident at all times of sudden disturbances. The veneer put on to make oneself " presentable " is too transparent to cover up improper antigravity adjustment ; but it is necessary to know what to look for. The person with inadequate antigravity adjustment excludes certain attitudes more or less totally according to the seriousness of his case.

We are generally concerned with what a person does or has achieved, rather than how he does it. On shifting our attention to examine the quality of the act, the ease, the time necessary to initiate an act, the amount of interference a person can stand before the act is upset—in short, if we examine the manner instead of the result of doing, the inadequate adjustment shows up much more readily.

We have seen previously that to eliminate the capacity of locomotion completely, nothing short of total destruction will do. Without legs, even without limbs altogether, moving along is still

possible. If we look at what is achieved without concern as to how
it is achieved, we could hardly tell a legless person from a normal
one ; both may have moved from the place in which we left
them to the new place where we now observe them. Only because
the way in which they achieve the displacement is so different, is
the difference between two such persons so outstanding. In acts
where the mechanisms at work are not readily observable, it is
difficult to tell a cripple from a normal person just by examining
the final result. We consider two fathers. The psychiatrist with
more intimate knowledge may find one a normal person and the
other a total wreck. When we are able to gain more intimate
knowledge of how people achieved the immediately apparent
success, we find so much misery behind the bright spots put out to
be seen, that many feel rather inclined to pity humanity as
a whole.

Anyone who has been able to give some sort of help or even
only hope, to bring about improvement, can tell of continuous
surprises to find among his callers people whom, in his ignorance,
he always considered as outstanding successes. He soon gets used
to it, and is not astonished to find first-rate athletes complaining
of premature ejaculation, successful dynamic financiers complaining of lack of interest in life, brilliant scientists who cannot
manage the experiment of marital life, painters who cannot love,
actors who stammer, etc.

We may conclude that the serious consequences of improper
adjustment to gravity are veiled in the same way as improper
development of the libido, or social adjustment, or any adaptation
for that matter.

It is obvious that in order to get some sense out of this complex
question it is necessary to have a clear idea of what is proper or
correct in human behaviour. There is usually a moral code
inherited from religious practice or social justice and convenience
lying behind all our activity. In general, the average behaviour is
the standard of good or fitting behaviour. This is a low minimum
indeed, far below the potential capacity of most of us. In modern
society specialisation is an absolute necessity. Obviously then
some of our potentialities must be in relative abeyance. My contention is that in properly mature persons no faculty and no
articulation is so utterly excluded from use directly or indirectly as
to render it unserviceable.

Man's capacity to make personal nervous and muscular patterns
was associated with the fact that innervations concerned with

voluntary movements grow while the control of action is being learned. All the new responses he acquires are integrated into a vast background of vegetative and reflex activity. He learns to speak, to walk, to adjust himself to his parents, and to other members of his society all at once. Concurrently, the libido shapes itself from primitive, diffuse, erotic urges, shifting from one object to another until it reaches a final stage of mature heterosexual character. All these different patterns developing simultaneously, are interwoven not only on the mental plane, but also in the body. To every attitude there corresponds not only an affective state, but a muscular pattern of the face as well as of all muscles in general.

We can therefore analyse the course of development of a personality by fixing our attention on one of these adjustments. Each of them may be chosen as representative of the individuality under examination. All of them have the disadvantage of depending upon and involving the subject himself in the procedure of his own analysis. In all, the vehicle by which the analysis is performed, is speech. This is, for the majority of people, a very clumsy means of conveying precise information. The same words often mean quite different things to different persons. To describe a movement or an event that can be seen in a fraction of a second, a cumbersome flow of words is necessary. Even then there is little precision in the description, and expressions like " you know what I mean " crop up sooner or later. Any visual and tactile evidence must therefore be considered as more reliable, as well as labour saving.

Taking this viewpoint with regard to the ground we have covered, it is quite obvious that the most suitable function for analysing the development of a personality is his muscular activity. The closer one looks into the problem, the clearer it becomes that this is correct. For instance, it is desirable to define clearly and precisely what constitutes proper behaviour. Well, what is a proper libido development or a proper adjustment to society ? It is hard to believe, yet it is a fact, that although the libido is the central problem of psychoanalysis, there is no clear and precise description of a proper sexual act, in all the classical literature on the subject. Because of correlation, however, the general trend of development can be studied in any function. Maturity of the antigravity function is apparent in the erect potent posture. It is much easier to define the potential erect posture, and we shall see in precise mechanical terms of what it consists.

It seems correct to think that all hindrance in the development of the libido will be noticeable primarily in the sexual act itself, and not only in secondary and auxiliary manifestations of the sexual instinct. If the average man's behaviour is neurotic, the sexual act of the average man is not what it might be potentially. By the principle of correlation, all adaptations and adjustments should bear the same general character. Maladjustment in respect of any adaptation should be, and is, observable in the antigravity function as well. It is known, in fact, from observation, that neurotic persons present peculiarities in the antigravity muscles. To cite Professor Josephine Rathbone :[1] " . . . it is quite safe to suggest one empirical hypothesis, which has grown out of observation of individuals who are having serious emotional difficulties. It appears that many of them lose the ability to stand in complete extension, and assume a position of more or less flexion."

How does this come about ?

Erect posture, for which the human body is best suited, is essentially such that little effort is required in maintaining it ; standing is a higher performance than advancing. Improper standing is arrested or incompleted learning. Moreover, greater muscular effort is necessary in standing without complete extension. As in all improperly performed acts, greater energy expenditure is involved in the case of improper standing. We have, however, seen that exteroceptive, proprioceptive, otolithic and labyrinthine reflexes are responsible for the posture of animals. In man, we said that the optical righting and the conscious function have an overriding influence, and that all the impulses are algebraically added to produce the result. Two alternatives could account for a person continuously maintaining a posture different from the one the reflex mechanisms are best fitted for. First, faulty mechanisms, either inherited or diseased. There are certainly such cases, but they give trouble from earliest infancy. Second, the conscious overriding control, all the elements of which are acquired through personal experience, is responsible for the faulty activity, In most cases anatomical lesion is excluded and we conclude that the overriding control gives directions contradicting the other reflex impulses from all the gravity-concerned centres. If this is the case, there must be muscular contraction present that is not indispensable for maintaining the proper erect posture. Unnecessary muscular contraction is, in fact, easy to demonstrate in all cases of improper posture. Close study shows

[1] *Corrective Physical Education* (Saunders), 2nd Edition, page 106.

that we deal with faulty distribution of activity, i.e., some muscular groups are doing unnecessary work while others are flabby and toneless.

Every function has its own vulnerable points, where most faults are likely to occur, In psychoanalysis we know of Oedipus complex, castration complex and the like These occur at crucial periods of development of the libido. And if the learning process is halted there, a clear case is present.

The adjustment to gravity has its own history with similar foci of arrested development. The spine, in early childhood, is practically straight, and the cervical curve begins to form before the lumbar curvature. Thus the shoulder, neck and sacro-lumbar regions are those in which most incomplete, or otherwise faulty, learning will find its halting barrier. These are mechanically the regions in which the greatest muscular adjustment is necessary, because very heavy masses have to be properly aligned with great precision. Also many of the muscles of these regions act on more than one joint, and their control is more delicate. Moreover, twisting of the body around the vertical axis, through the centre of gravity, for which the human frame is predominantly fitted, and which is a special advantage of the human erect posture, takes place mainly in these two regions.

With the head prevented from turning right and left on its support, and lumbar vertebrae made rigid too, turning of the body becomes an awkward, laborious and slow operation, necessitating at least three steps. We have seen in reviewing Magnus's work that these two regions play, in fact, a unique part in the antigravity muscular adjustment. They may be considered as a kind of sense organ. The neck and pelvis tonic standing and righting reflexes are initiated in the muscles of these regions.

If the conscious control or the optical righting reflexes are responsible for faulty posture, then their elimination should leave the lower centres in control, and a reduction of flexion should take place, and the carriage should become more erect. Under hypnotism and spontaneous somnambulic states, the head is, in fact, lifted and the pelvis straightened, so that the person stands taller than in his normal waking state. Blind people too, carry their head higher than the average. Thus, if an actor is to play the part of a blind man on the stage, it is enough for him to raise and immobilise the head in its rotation around the vertical axis, i.e., to turn the whole trunk with the head rigid but upright, to find the audience at once comprehending the situation.

In short, arrested development leaves its mark on all the functions without exception. Digestion, breathing, muscular control, sexual act and social adjustment are all affected simultaneously. Only deep emotional disturbances can so affect the conscious control as to distort the appreciation of the environment and yet leave the subject in ignorance to continue in an imaginary world of his own.

12. "MEASURING" POSTURE

EMOTIONS are essentially subjective, and only those who experience them have any idea of the comparative intensity of such experiences. However, there are somatic changes that give an indirect observable account of such reactions. This is particularly so in the case of anxiety states where the extensor inhibition is most marked. We have already mentioned the well-known fact that people with emotional trouble seem to be incapable of full extension.

Chronic anxiety, inhibiting the antigravity muscles, does, in fact, lead to attitudes with the extensors lacking normal tonus. In such cases, the subject will also frequently revert to conscious control of the highly unpleasant sensation in the pit of the stomach. Through the intimate relation of the vestibular excitation with the cardiac and diaphragmatic regions, holding breath and flexor contraction subdue these disagreeable reactions. In cases of long standing, these patterns integrate into the reflex pattern of erect carriage and carriage is no longer fully erect. Standing is now maintained with superfluous muscular tension, even when the centre of gravity is at its highest possible position. The cervical and lumbar curves are exaggerated and the lack of tonus in the antigravity muscles, especially of the shoulder-neck joints, and in the hip-pelvis region, will shift the centre of gravity forward. The toes will carry more weight than the flexor digitori can cope with permanently. They will contract strongly, and the toes will crook or buckle.

According to Lovett (*loc. cit. Rathbone*, p.88) : " When the body is in standing stable equilibrium the centre of gravity is just above and half way between the anterior superior illiac spines ; a vertical line dropped from the centre of gravity passes just in front of the knee and ankle joints, and touches the ground within the area between the feet—the underpropping area." Obviously the word " stable " equilibrium is improper mechanically, and should be replaced by " unstable." We feel stable with the centre of gravity as high as possible, because this position is the easiest to restore, as the nervous system is specially fitted for righting the body to it.

It feels stable by habit of reverting to it, but is mechanically, by definition, unstable.

In the cases of lack of tonus, and superfluous tension, as stated above, the centre of gravity would be anterior of the line given by Lovett, and the body prevented from falling by the continuous hyperextension of the knee joints and the cervical and lumbar curves. The toes would be carrying more weight than necessary, etc. This is borne out by experience.

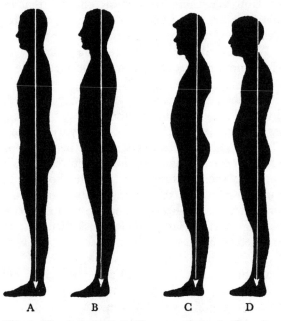

Fig. 3.—The vertical parallel lines were drawn by the writer.

In the cases where standing is maintained in conditions close to the potent posture, a vertical plane through the centre of gravity, and parallel to the shoulders passes approximately through the anterior part of the ankle joint and the entrance to the ear (external auditory meatus). On measuring the angle formed by a line joining the entrance to the ear and the anterior of the ankle joint, with the vertical at the ankle joint, people may be divided into four groups :

A	B	C	D
0°-0°15′	0°15′-0°45′	0°45′-1°30′	1′30°-2′0°

In practice, it is more convenient to measure the horizontal distance between these lines to a line at the level of the ear, and divide it by the vertical distance of the ear from the floor. This gives approximately :

A	B	C	D
0	15/1000	25/1000	35/1000

These are, however, tentative figures, as the number of measurements made is too small from a statistical point of view.

It may be interesting, in this connection, to state the following: There is a chart referred to as the Harvard University Chart[1], for grading body mechanics. This chart gives four silhouettes, reproduced in Fig. 3, corresponding to four grades.

Grade A. Excellent mechanical use of the body
1. Head straight above chest, hips and feet.
2. Chest up and forward.
3. Abdomen in and flat.
4. Back, usual curves not exaggerated.

Grade B. Good mechanical use of the body
1. Head too far forward.
2. Chest not so well up or forward.
3. Abdomen, very little change.
4. Back, very little change.

Grade C. Poor mechanical use of the body.
1. Head forward of chest.
2. Chest flat.
3. Abdomen relaxed and forward.
4. Back curves exaggerated.

Grade D. Very poor mechanical use of the body
1. Head still further forward.
2. Chest still flatter and further back.
3. Abdomen completely relaxed, " slouchy."
4. Back, all curves exaggerated to the extreme.

I have, as yet, been unable to come by the original and find out from what data these silhouettes were drawn. However, drawing four parallel lines normal to the horizontal shows clearly the increasing horizontal distance from the ear to the vertical plumb line passing through the centre of the ankle. It may thus be

[1]See, for example, *Body Mechanics in Health and Disease*, by Joel H. Goldthwait *et al.* (Lippincot & Co.)

possible to fix an index for grading body mechanics by the measurement of a single length, as described above. A large number of measurements must be made and examined before conclusions can be drawn.

This is not the only method of measuring how far the present state departs from the ideal potent state. The moment of inertia relative to the vertical axis through the centre of gravity should ideally be the smallest possible, compatible with the anatomy of the body. It is so where fully extended erect carriage is maintained tonically. To increase the moment of inertia of the human body, the centre of gravity must be lowered. While standing, this can be achieved by adopting an attitude similar to that of silhouette (D) in Fig. 3. Professor R. W. Pohl, of Göttingen University, has designed beautiful apparatus for showing large audiences that one can measure the moment of inertia of a man standing on a rotary table fitted with a calibrated coiled spring. The figures for different moments of inertia of the human body, given earlier, were taken from his book *Physical Principles of Mechanics and Acoustics*. On measuring the actual moment of inertia, and dividing it by the mass of the body, a ratio could be obtained that would be smallest for individuals with ideal carriage. Similar ratios could be established for all the four groups.

When proper erect standing is maintained with no superfluous muscular tension, all the interarticulation surfaces must be normal to the vertical, and every two arms of the articulation in a straight line. A percussion applied vertically upwards to a rigid board on which a person is standing, will be transmitted through the body to the skull, and through it to any pressure sensitive apparatus placed on it, more fully than when the articulations are hyperflexed and hyperextended. The efficiency of transmission will decrease from group A individuals to groups B, C and D, in whom it will be lowest. The above reasoning explains why people belonging to group D jump poorly, lift weights with difficulty, and tire when carrying additional weight, or the weight of their body only. They tire especially rapidly when running upstairs. On watching such performances, it is quite noticeable that little of the effort of the legs is transmitted to the upper thorax and head, which follow sluggishly, in spite of pronounced agitation of the limbs.

Every joint where the two members are inclined transmits a portion only of the force applied to either of them, and acts as a dash-pot, damping all transmission of mechanical stress through the joint. The soft, woolly punch of many boxers is due to faulty hip carriage, and no amount of training can ever make the punch " hard " so long as there are springy, flexed joints, at the instant of hitting.

I am quite aware that in practice, these methods are not more than an indication. It is important, however, that it is possible to obtain some sort of measurement, even though indirect, of what is usually considered unfathomable. I have little doubt that with the accumulation of extensive data, especially by the first and last methods, very useful information would be obtained.

13. THE SIXTH SENSE

THE proper erect posture is more efficient than others. The anti-gravity mechanisms tend to bring the body into vertical alignment, or more precisely, into a configuration where all the weight-bearing interarticulation surfaces are subjected to a normal compression only. Most of the advantages of unstable erect carriage are gone if this condition is not satisfied.

A few questions therefore arise :—

(1) What is it that enables those who use the proper or better way of doing to distinguish it from the other ways, and so continue in it?

(2) Why is it that those who have adopted an inferior procedure usually stick to it in spite of seeing examples of better use around them?

Is it that *je ne sais quoi*, that some people seem to have, sometimes spoken of as an instinct, a kind of sixth sense? Indeed, a sixth sense it is !—the kinaesthetic sense. It is the sense by which muscular motion, weight, position in space, etc., are perceived. The organs concerned with this sense are diffused all over the body. They are the proprioceptive nerve endings we have already described. The co-ordinating centre is the labyrinth.

The general principle at work is as follows. All sensations are related to the stimuli producing them in a fixed manner. For example, if you hold a 20 lb. weight in your hand and you shut your eyes, and if, noiselessly, a certain weight is added on to the weight you already carry, you will not become aware of it unless the additional weight is big enough to produce the *least detectable difference* in sensation. You won't notice a fly sitting on the 20 lb., but you will certainly become aware of the addition of a pound weight ; actually, you will probably detect half a pound, or even less, for the ratio for this kind of sensation is 1/20 to 1/40. This means that if you hold 1 lb. you should be able to detect the addition of 1/20 to 1/40 of a pound. In simple words, the Weber Fechner law means that the smaller the weight you are holding, the smaller is the added or subtracted portion that you will be able to notice.

This law applies roughly to all sensations—light, sound, heat, pain, smell, muscular effort, etc.

In precise terms, we say that there is a logarithmic relationship between sensation and stimulus, namely : " The difference in stimulus (I) that produces the least detectable difference in sensation (S) is always in the same ratio to the whole stimulus (I)." Thus :—

$$\Delta S = K \frac{\Delta I}{I} \text{ and } S = \mathrm{Log_e}\text{-}I + \mathrm{Const.}$$

This is known as the Weber Fechner law, which holds over the normal range of sensations.

People who apparently spontaneously prefer the better way of doing are those who have the capacity to detect small differences of sensation. All sensations in which muscular activity is involved are largely dependent on the smallest amount of tonus persistent in the musculature. When the tonus is the smallest possible, you sense the finest increase in effort. Easy and smooth action is obtained when the aim is achieved by the smallest amount of exertion, which, in turn, is obtained with the minimum tonus present. The smaller the stimulus present, the smaller is the change that we perceive, or are capable of detecting. When the proper erect posture is held, i.e., held with the minimum tone that is necessary, not only do we sense the smallest change, so that righting the position when necessary is started in good time, but the body is capable of righting itself immediately without preparation. Most apprenticeships begin with trial and error. People with a fine kinaesthetic sense tend to a low tonic contraction, and are not satisfied until they find the way of doing which involves the smallest amount of exertion ; also, the limit to which the unnecessary effort is eliminated, is closer to the ideal minimum. In our education stress is laid on the result, and not on the way of achieving it; even though it be at the expense of greater effort than is really necessary. At the higher level of effort, one cannot detect small differences ; therefore, it is impossible to improve beyond a certain stage. Thus, things are self-perpetuating ; the crude kinaesthetic sense tends to become cruder and cruder, the finer one tends to become finer yet.

Activity becomes habitual with repetition to which consent is given. The habitual mode of doing feels right because of repeated approval.

This answers the two questions, why some people spontaneously find the better way of doing, and stick to it, and why others, in spite of the example presented by other people, continue in their inferior way. They have no means of sensing the difference. Unless they become aware of it intellectually, they never know about it at all. Intellectual awareness is, however, not sufficient to alter matters fundamentally. For all they can do is to observe other people and imitate the grossly observable differences. Many people proceed on these lines all their life. They find that everything necessitates training and guidance. They never can play the piano properly, they cannot swim, dance or do anything in that marvellous way in which " talented " people just pick things up from nowhere. They would need to relive their lives several times to have the leisure to train, i.e., to imitate the outward differences of doing of all that is admirable in other people's activity.

However, things do not generally deteriorate beyond repair, because of the greater importance of learning in men. The overriding control of the conscious makes it possible to improve any act of doing even though the way of performing it is not the proper way. This is achieved by detour means and waste of effort. And so people walking in the most awkward way may walk as fast as anybody. The fact that the end can, most of the time, be achieved equally well, irrespective of the amount of effort involved in achieving it, is very fortunate, as it makes life possible for a large number of imperfect doers.

The process examined is, so to·speak, a closed circle, self-compensated and sufficient for a certain mode of existence, fixed at an inferior level. In normal conditions, it makes little difference whether a person has a fine kinaesthetic sense or not. There is usually sufficient time for apprenticeship, and to the outside world it is immaterial how much effort is put into an act, provided the end is achieved. When a screw has to be driven, it is of little importance whether the screwdriver is used skilfully or not ; it might even be driven with a knife. Rare and essentially non-repetitive actions can be carried out in this fashion. If one, or only a few screws are to be put in, the knife may not suffer too much, and the screws might be reasonably well driven in. In habitual and constantly recurring actions, it is essential to preserve the tool. In the living organism, the tool must improve by use, otherwise perfect action is possible only for a short time. If a knife is used for screwing a large number of screws, it becomes useless as a knife and as a screwdriver.

The proper way of doing must leave the tool in a good and, if possible, improved condition. Unskilful doing uses up more energy than proper doing. The part of the energy which is not accountable for in the act performed is used up in affecting the tool, the organs and the other mechanisms involved in the act. No action is ideally efficient, i.e., the total energy involved is always greater than that accountable for in the action performed. The difference in the living organism is sensed as difficulty. Efficient activity is sensed as easy and fluent, and, for reasons we cannot discuss at the moment, looks and feels graceful. People with a low kinaesthetic sense feel only extreme inefficiency. However, they sometimes succeed by pure chance in performing a certain act in a more efficient way than usual, and are exalted by that sensation of fluency which the people with a fine kinaesthetic sense experience most of the time. We are usually induced to think that constant training brings about that happy mode of doing.

To a certain degree this is true. Especially when the person from whom we learn, or whom we imitate without his consent, has a fine kinaesthetic sense. But even an imperfect mode of doing feels better and better because it becomes habitual, and some of what we regarded as internal friction is lessened by the repetition. So that feeling right is associated with relative improvement only, but is in no way a warrant of correctness of doing.

We are in a vicious circle. Those who have a fine kinaesthetic sense continue improving, and those who have not, continue deteriorating. The importance of heredity cannot be denied. But its importance is not final, nor need it be exaggerated. We have seen the influence of learning, and know that a fine kinaesthetic sense can be thrown out of gear by adopting the improper course. We have also seen the mechanism of such mishappenings. The human facility for learning can be used to yield bad results with good tools, just as it can be used to achieve good results with bad ones. We have, in fact, seen that conscious interference is at the root of both alternatives. The same means must be used to learn the proper method of doing. Provided conscious consent and approval can be secured for the better method, the direction can easily be changed from constant deterioration to constant improvement. The inheritance will only fix the rate of improvement, and therefore, because of the limited spell of life, also the final level that can be reached. It is not unreasonable to expect that the more balanced use of the nervous system achieved by adopting the better use of oneself, will lengthen life. We know, in fact, that the majority of deaths result from exhaustion of some vital parts, while the rest follow into the grave with unspent vitality. A better use should make the wear and tear more uniform, so that the total frame can spend itself evenly. Changing the direction of development from deterioration to improvement is thus, on the whole, setting right the average inequality of inheritance.

14. NORMAL GRAVITATION ADJUSTMENT

THE first co-ordinated manifestation of the antigravity function is the reflex response of the vestibular apparatus to sharp change of position and withdrawal of support, expressed in a general contraction of the flexor muscles. Next, loud noises begin to elicit a similar response. These reactions are the result of stimulation of the vestibular nerve which, at the same time, starts a chain of vegetative vaso-motor reactions. The conditioning to loud noises is thus integrated into the background of pre-existing nervous and muscular and vegetative affective patterns that are linked together.

Soon, the eyes begin to follow light, the head turning to assist the eyes. When the apprenticeship in the right-left movement is well on the way, downward movements of the eyes and then upward begin. Then raising of the head is learned, followed by hyperextensions. The intervals between these phases are short and ill-defined ; the general trend is, however, clear. Sitting up, twisting of the body, crawling, then walking and finally, unsupported standing are learned. Running and jumping follow normally.

During all this period, the child indulges in rolling on the ground from right to left and vice versa ; he will now turn himself around in the standing position and will persist in this activity in spite of continuous warnings against falling and giddiness.

To complete the antigravity adjustment to its potential perfection, he must learn to balance easily and securely on one leg, to jump, to turn himself round, and finally perform all these movements *with the eyes shut.*

A coherent picture of the whole course of adaptation to gravity is obtained if the head is regarded as the support of the teleceptors, i.e., the instruments through which our relations with the outside world are extended beyond our body.

Thus, the initial apprenticeship of the movements of the head is associated with the vestibular apparatus reflectively, without any personal experience being necessary. The anatomy of the head determines the conditioning of response to sound, and the reflective response to gravity. Next, the motility of the eyes is integrated into the already existing basic movements of the head. The first manifestations of consciousness will appear with the control of the head which allows the child to follow and direct itself towards moving objects or sources of sound.

Soon afterwards, the head begins to right itself to a special position in which the plane of the occipital opening indicating the anatomical orientation of the head on the atlas, is slightly rising forward (about 15 degrees in European races), the orbicular axis being horizontal and the otolithic maculae at 145 degrees. At the beginning, the head tends reflectively to this position, in whatever position the body may be. A baby, put on its tummy, lifts its head to this reference position, and remains that way as long as necessary. The tonic muscular contraction is practically indefatigable. With this position of the head is associated the image of oneself in one's relation to space. And for correct appreciation of spatial relation, all acts involve a brief fixing of the head in it. Standing up, or changing attitude are sensed to be accomplished when the head assumes the reference position. Only after this can a new act be initiated without the reflex impulses contradicting voluntary control.

The rest of the adjustment to gravity may be considered as learning to maintain the head in this position while raising it higher and higher. In the sitting position, the rotation of the head twists the neck muscles and the body learns to follow it so as to re-establish symmetrical proprioceptive impulses. The cervical curve is forming during this period. When, thanks to crawling, the hip control is learned and the joints are strong enough to permit their extension against the full weight of the body, movements forward are attempted. A little later, the rotation apprenticeship is resumed with the additional twisting in the lumbar region and hip joints. Again, twisting of the head, which is now followed by the thorax more fully, twists the lumbar muscles and ligaments, and the pelvis moves by the aid of the legs so as to establish symmetrical proprioceptive incitations in the twisted parts.

With every phase of this development, the breathing mechanism is altered as different parts of the trunk become rigid, and the parts that are left free to contract and expand are different. Thus, in the lying position breathing is assured by the diaphragm movement and the lower ribs. In the sitting position the breathing is strongly affected by the tonus of the abdominal wall, and the lateral ribs expansion is more pronounced. In standing, while holding on to something for support, and before the lumbar curve is formed, the pectoral muscles and the extensors of the back make the chest rigid, preventing movement of the upper ribs almost completely. In fact, there are as many breathing mechanisms as distinct attitudes of the body. In proper development, breathing follows a definite rhythm, unhampered by the position of the body.

All effort by the limbs necessitates rigidity of the trunk. This is increased to its maximum when the ribs are fixed and the breath is held in the position of inspiration. However, in proper body mechanics, the breathing rhythm is not interrupted, even in violent efforts. When the pelvis is held properly the lower abdomen feels full and forward, the rigidity required for efficient use of the arms is obtained while diaphragmatic breathing is maintained evenly and effortlessly. In normal development of the antigravity function, no awareness is necessary to bring about such a configuration of the body segments. Correction of faulty breathing by any method fails in all sudden efforts, so long as the erect posture, and especially the pelvis position, is incorrect.

With the completion of the learning of the pelvis control, the formation of the arches of the foot is well on the way. The transversal arch forms after the longitudinal one. The adjustment to gravity, like all nerve functions, can have a simple eventless history, or one of favourable and unfavourable accidents. Like all nerve functions, the earlier the development, the stabler the function. The later phases of development are vulnerable and more easily destroyed than the earlier ones. This is true to the extent that the later phases, which approach the cultivating of the function to the ideal potential capacity, often never develop fully. Just as in any other adjustment, the final stages of maturity are more often than not unfinished. Very few people, in fact, accomplish a full independence of the mother or father image, but continue it in their marital relations, and with those in authority. Concurrently few people bring the learning of the antigravity skill to full maturity.

At the passage from one stage of development to the next, there is always the possibility of relapsing back into a previous stage. Many children begin to walk, then stop for some time, and try again later on ; or begin to speak and then forget until some time later. These are very serious events. They are often provoked by very well meaning parents who encourage children to hurry on before sufficient learning has taken place in the preceding phase.

Attempts to do things before their time will be associated with risk, and effort, and compromise the sense of security. Children who grow in such conditions will need encouragement, compliments and goading in all enterprise later, and are likely to give up any new task in which they do not find an immediate success to begin with.

Besides these general effects on character and behaviour, somatic faulty development ensues. Thus, playpens, and guidance by parents to use them as support, bring about premature prolonged standing before sufficient extension of the hip joints has been made possible by an adequate period of crawling. The child becomes conditioned to associate standing with an improper muscular pattern, because, at that stage, the lumbar curve is not yet formed, neither is the musculature of the lower abdominal wall.

Children are also required to sit still for long periods and fix their attention on the blackboard or on the book, before their neuromuscular mechanisms are good enough to do so. Immobility is more difficult than movement, and must be learned very gradually. Children must be allowed to shift their eyes as much as they like, and learn to see while scanning rapidly, and not by prolonged fixing, if they are to have good eyesight. It should be remembered that the pyramidal tract which transmits impulses to the voluntary muscles is not fully developed, even when the child has already learned to walk. (Some medullation of these nerves continues up to the age of twenty and even later, so that improvement in muscular control by sheer growth of the nerves is going on up to that age.)

15. TONIC ADJUSTMENT

GREAT division between theory and practice is found in the methods of curing emotional and physical arrested development. Most of the theories speak of " biological entity," or " man must be considered as a whole," " unity " and " globality." But in practice, each school deals directly with but one little part of the personality ; so much so, that even the psyche is subdivided in psychiatric practice and the body in physical re-education. One school sees the whole personality in the social function, another in the libido, etc. In the physical methods, there is a similar position ; one school teaches relaxation because hypertonic contraction is found together with emotional trouble, others only see the flaccidity and flabbiness of the antagonists of the contracted muscles ; for generalised rigidity is rare, except in very serious neurological cases[1]. One school strengthens the " weak " abdominal wall, the next, some other weakness.

Thus theory and practice are as far asunder as before the idea of unity was ever advanced. Fortunately, it is only what is effectively done that has any real value. And in practice, it is quite impossible to influence one function in strict isolation from all the others, so that all methods have a measure of success. But the success is due very largely to indirect and unintended effects, and only partially to the avowed and purported action.

Even from this study, it is shown sufficiently clearly, I hope, that fear, for instance, is as much a problem of the body as it is of the psyche. Complete relief from fear is quite impossible by acting on either exclusively. It is true that the psychic complex can be resolved by psychiatric treatment, just as the muscular and vegetative fear pattern can be resolved by somatic treatment. But as there is no psychic fear alone, nor physical fear alone, either treatment alone is no more than a partial solution of fear in the total personality, and can have no claim to completeness. Moreover, it is impossible to resolve fear without affecting, indirectly, sleep, the digestive, sexual, social and motility functions at the same time. Only on an intellectual plane can the isolation of one

---

[1] See *L'Hypertonie de Décérébration chez l'Homme*, by P. M. Mollaret and I. Bertrand (Masson & Cie).

117

function be theoretically perceived, and everybody is agreed that pure intellectual understanding has very little effect on the personality. Notwithstanding this general agreement, the emotional plane is reached in practice through intellectual understanding and analysis. The real difference is merely in the degree of directness of the method, and in nothing else. What actually occurs are sensory-intellectual-emotional-somatic reactions which are indivisible. Consequently, not only the emotional, but also the vegetative and somatic planes must be reached before there is total personality readjustment. All these planes must be equally directly dealt with in order to make prompt and lasting readjustment possible. A rational systematic course is suggested hereafter, in which we begin with somatic re-education ; the reason for this choice will become obvious and self-evident.

Unused parts of the body grow weak and become atrophied ; other parts bear a correspondingly heavier burden and are overworked ; and the body becomes a caricature of the human frame. Fatigued motor cells become inhibitory nuclei, and a whole series of acts become excluded and impossible. Rationally, we convince ourselves that we do not really want, or that it is right that we should not want to perform such acts, and they are totally withdrawn from our repertory of normal use. Next to total withdrawal from use, is pre-selected discrimination of acts, so as to avoid certain configurations or muscular patterns. In the long run, the result is the same.

Only the *tonically* erect state provides equal opportunity for all acts and muscular combinations. No other configuration possesses the dynamic qualities proper to unstable equilibrium, and no other is desirable except as a transitory posture or attitude which should never become permanent.

When the head and pelvis are properly held, all the range of their movements, and those of the rest of the body are used, explored or tried, normally, without any special attention. When they are not, the attitude or posture can be likened to a groove into which the person sinks never to leave unless some special force makes him do so. With time, the groove deepens, and stronger forces are necessary to remove him from it. Thus, once the sunken head posture is acquired, a person will revert to the most awkward and tiresome (to normal people) procedure in turning his head, but will obstinately avoid lifting it into that position from which turning is normally easy. A parallel procedure is observed on the emotional plane, where the immature person uses detour, roundabout ways instead of direct, simple methods.

In the long run, deformation sets in. The gaping side of articulations fill with fibrous textures, especially between vertebrae, where there is very little movement in general. Ligaments shorten, some muscles become too strong, and others atrophy. Very wonderful X-ray photographs of such deformations can be found in *Body Mechanics* by Goldbraith *et al.*, as we have already mentioned.

These deformations show that the faulty position is maintained constantly with very rare breaks, day and night. Thus, permanent deformation due to faulty posture sets in and purely orthopaedic methods are used to correct them.

To alter faulty habitual erect carriage is, in everybody's opinion, a very difficult enterprise. Especially striking is the case of persons seeking guidance of their own initiative. From the obstinate resistance encountered in such cases, it is obvious that what is attempted is really a major operation on the personality of the subject. All workers in this field agree on this point. To cite a very cautious writer who insists on open-mindedness, Professor Rathbone says :—[1]

" It has been the experience of those who have tried to correct a condition of forward head and neck that it is one of the most difficult propositions in corrective exercise."

For the subject may understand that it is desirable to alter his body mechanics and wish it, too ; but for years having given consent to one mode of carriage, he feels right and comfortable only in that one. Though the correct position is better, and theoretically easier, he feels strained in it, firstly because it is new to him, and secondly because the deformation that has set in, because of his habitual carriage, is an extra hindrance. Thus, the posture, the essence of which is minimal effort, cannot be assumed without considerable and marked strain.

It is a vicious circle indeed, as the subject makes strenuous efforts to relax or to do something effortlessly. It is the manner of doing that is to be altered, whereas all the usual methods involve simply the application of the faulty manner of doing to learning some new acts only. In every exercise, one particular point is altered, while all the rest continues in the old manner. The old manner of doing is thus also brought into action, and is exercised as well. The only slightly altered act is preconditioned to feel

[1] (*loc. cit.*, page 56.)

awkward, strenuous and even painful. The new posture can be held only as long as there is conscious attention. As soon as this relaxes, and it does in all sharp demands of the environment, the habitual, faulty manner is elicited automatically. The extinction of the old conditioning continues alongside the formation of the new habit. Alternately, the old one is re-established and rein-forced, and the new one is inhibited, and vice versa. The result is slow progress, with frequent periodic relapses into the old manner of doing, inevitably accompanied by disappointment and discouragement.

Different suggestions have been made to break this vicious circle. One theory is that the feet should be re-educated first, the reason being that they carry the whole body. Another is that the movements of the head should come first, This is a more sensible suggestion, considering what we know already. Whatever we start with, however, is of no avail, so long as we have not solved the problem of making the new and proper pattern feel right, and conscious attention superfluous.

This is the essence of the problem. The well adapted person feels right only when he does the right thing—the ill adapted feels right while doing the wrong thing. The fact that he knows it, does not help him any more than the neurotic is helped by know-ing that his behaviour is abnormal. The solution is found in the criticism made of the method used. It is obvious that the subject must not be called on to do anything that involves his habitual response to gravity. For while standing or sitting, the detail of changing the position of the head is insignificant in comparison with the total volume of habitual action present. If he could be screened from gravity altogether, there would be no necessity at all to unlearn the old patterns of doing. The next best we can do, therefore, is to lie flat on the floor. We free the central nervous system from the habitual exteroceptive impulses arriving through the soles of the feet, and change most of the proprioceptive im-pulses of the whole body, the otolithic and optical impulses in-cluded. The subject is practically free from all stimulus evoking his habitual response to gravity. He is free from the major anti-gravity activity of his muscles and nervous centres as much as possible. (There is, of course, the possibility of immersion in a liquid of prearranged density which would be useful in certain cases. It may be worth looking into this possibility more closely.)

We have seen that the stimulus sensation relation is such that the smaller the stimulus, the finer is the increment that we are able to detect. So that once an unnecessary contraction is established, the sensitivity is reduced and a continually deteriorating situation is established. On the other hand, were it possible to increase the sensitivity, the same law would act so as to decrease the contraction. For smaller increments would be sensed as a strain and, would feel wrong. The process would tend to educate the subject to feel wrong in the same manner as the man with proper gravity adjustment. This would be a complete solution of the problem. The next step is, therefore, reduction of the habitual unnecessary strain where it exists, without direct conscious attention. The reader will remember that in faulty carriage, the lumbar and cervical curves are maintained in the lying position exactly as when standing. Obviously, the minimum contraction detectable as such is sufficient to maintain the curvatures, in spite of the gravitational forces now acting so as to flatten them.

The next step then, is to reduce these curves, i.e., to reduce the minimum contraction sensed. Lifting the head off the ground involves contraction of the flexors of the neck, now used as anti-gravity muscles. Their antagonists, the extensors, relax accordingly. For the first time then, the extensors of the head are forced reflectively to a lower state of contraction than the subject is normally used to associate with the sensation of " no effort." In bad cases, the contraction of the extensors is lowered even beneath the level of their contraction during sleep. For bad, highly neurotic cases maintain the cervical and lumbar curves rigidly in the same form, even during sleep. They wake up with a sense of tiredness and stiffness of the neck and spine which are only to be expected.

We have thus achieved our aim ; we have succeeded in lowering the threshold of contraction below the habitual one without direct conscious attention, and without involving more than a small number of muscles, none of which are conditioned with the habitual response to gravity. And we leave the subject to learn the " feel " of reduced contraction of the neck extensors.

It must be noted that the motor centres and neurons concerned may be given their first rest for long years. In bad, longstanding cases, this is certainly so. The subject feels a queer sensation at the back of the neck ; also, the flexors of the neck being abnormally weak he cannot maintain the position for more than twenty seconds or so. He is not to be conditioned to feeling strain with the correct muscular habit and should be encouraged to give up and rest the head on the ground at the first impulse to do so.

After a few repetitions the subject becomes aware of the abdominal muscles contracting when lifting the head. And he generally asks if he is supposed to draw up his knees ; he feels he would be more comfortable in that position.

The abdominal contraction is necessary to anchor the chest and the sternum to which the neck flexors are fixed. The abdominal flexors contracting, their antagonists (the spinal erectors) decontract, and the lumbar curve now follows the same steps as the cervical one. The abdominal contraction is difficult and awkward with the legs extended ; on drawing up the knees the lumbar curve flattens out completely and the lower back touches the ground. The subject has then begun to feel an urge to do the right thing, and feels wrong when he should—the very aim we set out to achieve. People with good body mechanics, if requested to " lie down and then lift the head " do spontaneously draw up their knees unless the order is so worded as to prevent them from doing so.

After a few trials, every subject becomes aware that the head lift consists of two movements. One is where the head and neck are held and moved together, relative to the body. This movement is predominant at the initial phase of lifting the head off the ground. The neck stops moving later, while the second movement, that of the head relative to the neck, with the chin being drawn in, becomes predominant. Not only does the subject become aware of these differences, but he eagerly seeks guidance as to which of the movements he should prefer. We are obviously on the right track, as we have initiated a process operative in proper development, namely, awareness of small differences in doing, and urge to pick the better mode.

A priori there is nothing to choose between the two modes of lifting the head off the ground, as both achieve this in some measure. However, the proper way is to bring the head into such a position as to establish its normal relation to space and gravity, i.e., with the orbital axis horizontal. All people with good body mechanics are not satisfied, and feel the action incompleted until the position of the head has assumed this relation to space.

Several remarkable things are to be noted. First, that people with hyperextended neck muscles cannot at once bring the head into the proper postion ; the flexors being contracted, the extensors relax and lengthen beyond their habitual capacity ; they are nevertheless too stiff and short ; learning is necessary before they will increase to the proper length. Until then, they are being stretched. It is, therefore, essential not to force the pace, otherwise pain will follow. This is to be avoided, not only because of the suffering involved—which, by the way, is quite bearable—but because feeling right in the presence of pain cannot be conditioned without conscious intervention. Soon the cervical extensors become more elastic, and lose their stringlike texture ; the head comes nearer to the normal position. Further attempts will gradually lengthen reflectively and then stretch the muscles lower down, i.e., the extensors of the neck-shoulder articulation, until the chin can be lowered and the normal relation of the head to the vertical be resumed.

We must now consider in some detail the effect of stretching muscles, and in particular the extensor muscles. If a tendon or a muscle is cut (*in situ*) and pulled so as to stretch the muscle, the muscle pulls back. When there is no pull the muscle loses tone. With increased pull the tension in the muscle increases. This is Liddell's and Sherrington's stretch reflex. The reflex involved arises from the muscle itself, as severing the sensory nerve only, abolishes the reflex, though the motor nerve is intact. The reflex is therefore elicited only if the sensory impulses from the muscle are allowed to reach the necessary relay which will excite the motor nerve. There are stretch receptors in the muscle which are excited when the muscle is elongated passively.

We have seen that in a decerebrated animal the tone of the extensors is so exaggerated as to produce decerebrated rigidity. In the intact animal the proprioceptive impulses involved in standing originate in the stretch receptors. Though there is some stretch reaction in flexors, there is no sustained stretch reaction in them.

Two phases can clearly be distinguished in muscle stretching. First, the contraction is proportional to the elongation or stretching. Next, if the stretching ceases, the muscle starts contracting and a state of contraction persists for a long time afterwards. This is the second phase of fundamental importance in posture. The normal relation of the segments is resumed slowly and in steps, often in synchronism with the respiratory movements.[1] In all cases where gravity tends to produce flexion, as in the knee, hip or neck, when the articulation begins to flex it is extended by the stretch reflex. The rate of impulse discharge of the motor neurons in the stretch reaction is very slow (about eight per second) and fatigue does not occur. Adaptation in stretch receptors is

[1] See *L'Hypertonie de Décérébration chez l'Homme*, page 7.

slow and trains of impulses persist along the afferent fibres from the muscles as long as the stretch is maintained. When the stretch increases, more and more motor neurons are brought into action, and the contraction is sustained and as strong as the stretching force.

We may now return to our subject, left lying with his head lifted off the floor, and gradually trying to bring it to its normal relation with the vertical. To begin with, the flexors of the neck have assumed an antigravity activity and their antagonists have correspondingly relaxed and lengthened. Persistence in the same position fatigues the flexors which are suited for rapid, phasic action, but are ill fitted to replace the slow, strong and tonically contracting extensors. The tonus of the extensors continues to decrease reflectively, and they lengthen until they can yield no more. After that, lowering the chin stretches all the extensors of the cervical region. The subject, rising from the floor and re-suming his habitual standing, finds, however, the slow after-effect of the stretch reflex continuing for a considerable time, i.e., the head is raised to a higher position reflectively and, what is essential, without any conscious volition. His head tends, there-fore, towards the proper erect holding by the same mechanism as in people who spontaneously adopt proper posture, and not by conscious attention. Even if he ignores all we have said about him, his head will now be nearer to the proper position for a much longer period than he has spent on the floor. Moreover, less effort is necessary to maintain the head in a position nearer to the vertical than before. Therefore, he will, with time, become aware of smaller increments than usual and will feel awkward in his habitual position. He will then tend away from the old pattern, and will be launched on a self-correcting and improving course instead of one that constantly worsens and deteriorates. It is perhaps worth mentioning that active phase stretching of ex-tensors has quite a different effect altogether. The extensors are stretched positively while tonically contracted. Stretching, when there is nothing to make the extensors relax, excites mainly the pain receptors, and elicits further defence contraction. Insistence, in such cases hurts the muscles, and pain persists for several days.

The next remarkable thing is that the subject on the ground, with his knees drawn up and the head raised to the normal spatial position and the lumbar curve flattened, is in the attitude the body assumes reflectively in its reaction to falling. We have seen, in fact, that the inborn reaction to falling, when elicited in a newborn baby, consists in a complete contraction of the flexor system, and that if this is maintained, excitation abates. This attitude is associated with a sensation of safety[1]. Indeed, after a few seconds of maintaining the proper position, with the flattened lumbar curve, breathing becomes deep, regular and very smooth, accompanied by a general feeling of poise and peace.

The third remarkable thing is that the mechanism for instilling tone in the neck extensors, arrived at after a laborious analysis, is, in fact, the one used by nature in the normal development of every baby, and could have been discovered by observation. At the beginning, while lying on its back, the head is lifted by flexor contraction of the anterior of the body in reflex reactions until the baby can reproduce the same voluntarily. By that time sufficient tone has been developed in the neck extensors so that the head will not drop forward when the flexors are strong enough to raise the body to the sitting position. The neck extensors had little activity for lack of impulses from other sources. Only in its third month [2] does a baby occasionally begin to arch its body, pressing its head backwards.

Normal elasticity is developed and maintained in a muscle by the stretching that its antagonists give it. In the first few weeks a baby only flexes the head. In general, flexion predominates in the first month, then extension movements predominate and so on, until sitting is possible. That the muscle control and elasticity is not due only to the growth of the pyramidal tract, can be seen from the fact that babies away from their mothers, who are raised and lowered only for feeding and otherwise unavoidable occasions—and therefore, less frequently than when in their mothers' care—are, in fact, slower in their antigravity apprenticeship. They will make attempts to sit up much later. With no contraction actually taking place and tone in the antigravity muscles insufficient to maintain the body upright, sitting will appear much later. Even when helped to sit up, first the head, then the thorax drop forward, and baby finds itself lying on its side. Contractions do, therefore, play an important rôle in the development of control and elasticity in muscles.

Without going into full details, we may say that we rebuild the entire frame following the course outlined in the beginning of

[1]See *The Body Pattern of Anxiety*, page 92.
[2]See *Les Manifestations Motrices Spontanées chez l'Enfant*, by Marcel Bergeron(Herman & Cie, Paris).

the chapter "Normal Gravitation Adjustment," keeping in mind that :—

(1) In normal learning, conscious awareness should gradually vanish, and so long as there are habitual proprioceptive impulses which have to be contradicted by the conscious control, the latter is taxed with an extra burden of constant attention—a burden unknown to normally matured people.

(2) Phasic movements are normally not attempted until after considerable tonic postural apprenticeship. The correction of the kinaesthetic sense and control should be well on the way before phasic movements are taught, so that properly integrated responses to gravitation are spontaneously elicited.

(3) Relaxation and strengthening of muscular groups must therefore not be attempted directly, but through their antagonists as in normal growth.

(4) The effect of gravitation should be eliminated as far as possible until the full range of flexibility of the neck and hip articulations is restored.

(5) Initially, the time necessary for the stretch reflex to become fully operative, is an essential factor. Experience suggests two to three minutes as the longest interval for maintaining any attitude.

Before re-education is achieved, any exercise in which the above points are ignored only presents the faulty doer with another opportunity of exercising his faulty manner of doing.

16. BODY AND EMOTIONS

IT is maintained by some that the body expresses the emotion initiated at the centre. Others, such as William James, maintain that we are gay because we laugh, i.e., the emotion at the centre follows a peripheral somatic disturbance or change. What seems to happen is that a sensory impulse evokes an emotive charge in the thalamus while the body response takes place. The body attitude maintains the affective state through the irregular pattern until the system recovers from the disturbance.

The important thing to us is that all sensory and motor experience is accompanied by emotional discharge of some sort; and that voluntary muscular patterns corresponding to these emotions are preceded by sensory experience and apprenticeship. Many have observed that complete extension seems unnatural, and often impossible to people who have emotional difficulties. It is common knowledge also that the expression of emotions is clearly seen on the face.

'An invaluable study of the relation of emotions to specific muscular patterns can be found in Darwin's *The Expression of Emotions in Man and Animals*. A clear distinction must be made between spontaneous and voluntary expression of emotions. Voluntary mimicry is initiated in the cortex and needs visual experience and memory. Thus, the blind spontaneously express anger or fear normally, but fail to reproduce the proper expression voluntarily or to order. Those that are not congenitally blind and have had visual experience of such expressions, behave like normal people (G. Dumas.). People suffering from Parkinson's disease express no spontaneous or voluntary emotion. In other diseases (pseudo-bulbar) the muscular patterns of different expressions are apparent but no emotion is experienced.

In every event there are three features to be considered ; the perception, which is the realisation of the material fact of a sensory nerve ending irritation ; the sensation, which is the integration of the state of self at the moment that the irritation has reached and affected the nervous system ; and finally, the psycho-somatic (mind-body) reaction.

In every conscious reaction, perception becomes sensation when our interest is in what happens at the moment in our body, rather than outside it. The image of our body and its relation to space is an essential element in every sensation.

A sensory experience receives its affective charge when the excitation reaches the thalamus. From the thalamus the excitation travels simultaneously in three directions ; the pallido striated motor system, where it elicits the spontaneous motor response ; the vegetative centres, where it elicits the emotional response ; and the cortex, where the conscious qualities of clarity, precision and awareness are formed. All the three centres are reached by the excitation from the thalamus practically simultaneously, and it is the conscious integration in the cortex that will either inhibit, enhance or modify the state created by the initial perception. There is, therefore, no fixed rule for what we are consciously aware in each case. It largely depends on the state of the frame at the moment of the experience, and essentially on the history of the neuromuscular mechanisms in question. In the case of complete maturity of the individual, the conscious integration over-rules all the others most of the time ; at lower levels, the vegetative state predominates, but in either case, the actually prevailing muscular pattern at the moment will greatly influence the course of the reaction.

There is always an element of inherited spontaneous mimicry due to the excitation of the pallido striated motor system and the vegetative centres, which the conscious enhances and clarifies into an emotion to be maintained.   This explains quite readily the formation of habitual posture as the result of emotional experience.

The essentially individual peculiarities in muscular habits are only partially due to congenital anatomical peculiarities. Habitual muscular patterns deriving from the voluntary system are, on the whole, the result of the sensory and muscular experience of the individual. Congenital anatomical peculiarities would normally remain insignificant without somatic and muscular habits formed by persistently recurring emotional states. Facilitated nervous paths are formed for muscular patterns conditioned by the environment to emotional states. These patterns, becoming habitual, fix the emotional disposition, that is, the individual's character.

In short, a recurrent emotional state always appears together with the attitude of the body and the vegetative state with which it was conditioned earlier. Therefore, when an emotional complex has been resolved, a specifically individual body habit is resolved simultaneously. I contend that all successful analysis, whatever technique is employed, is invariably accompanied, and probably preceded, by an alteration of posture and a change of muscular habit both in body and face.

17. MUSCULAR HABIT AND THE SEXUAL ACT

COITUS is a pleasurable act. At first sight such a statement may seem superfluous. But a surprisingly large number of people confuse in this context excitement with pleasure. Close examination of considerable numbers of people shows that, paradoxically, many do not experience any pleasurable feeling. Rather, there is a passionate excitement, or simply excitement and expectation of sublime satisfaction—which latter, however, does not materialise. With the approach of the climax, the excitation begins to peter out instead of building up, and the climax itself is not particularly memorable or pleasant. Such people come to believe that the excitement they experience is all that there is to it. In others, however, the sexual act produces a keen sensation of well-being. Mental and physical tension are released in a fashion that cannot be obtained in any other way.

In the average person, that is, in the great majority of people, and particularly in women, there is a constant striving for such a state, that is rarely satisfied. They are more or less indifferent to intercourse. They often feel even disgust, and regret having succumbed to the temptation once more.

This is one of the many forms of incomplete maturity of the personality. A parallel arrested maturity can be found in all those functions that need apprenticeship, in the antigravity adaptation, and in the social adjustment, as well as in the libidinal development.

In the antigravity function, full maturity is achieved when the nervous system and the executive organs maintain the whole frame in the potent state. That is, the state in which the directives issued from the conscious control can be promptly executed by the lower centres without any of the reflex impulses being contradicted.

In the sexual function we can distinguish a similar state descriptive of maturity. The release of tension in the culmination of the sexual act is essentially a vegetative phenomenon. It is a state that follows a reflex discharge starting when the excitation during coitus reaches a certain level. Reflexes do not manifest themselves properly when voluntary skeletal muscles are involved unless the conscious control is smoothly and completely withdrawn. Our education is such that most people feel it impossible, indecent, shameful or animal-like to relinquish this control, even when sexually excited. Properly matured people learn readily to do so after some experience. The majority, however, do not. Some try to bring about the reflex action by a conscious effort, just as some try to produce erection consciously. With apprenticeship, some sort of result can be obtained. Even then, the reflex is emptied of its essential property of being purely reflective.

Charles Darwin[1] relates the following incident, to show that conscious wish to perform a reflex action is sometimes sufficient to stop it or interrupt it even when there is stimulation that is normally infallible. Here it is :

" . . . many years ago I laid a small wager with a dozen young men that they would not sneeze if they took snuff, although they all declared that they invariably did so ; accordingly they all took a pinch, but from wishing much to succeed, not one sneezed, though their eyes watered, and all without exception, had to pay me the wager." He next cites Sir H. Holland as saying that attention paid to the act of swallowing interferes with the proper movements, and that this at least partly accounts for the difficulty people experience in swallowing pills.

In some people it is difficult to elicit the knee jerk reflex in the usual way, though the arc is intact. It is the usual practice to clasp hands with such a person and ask him to squeeze at the appropriate moment. As the conscious control is involved in the act of squeezing the reflex is freed from its inhibitory influence and appears (if the arc is intact) while the person squeezes.

I know of no exception to the rule that all people with emotional trouble do not experience adequate pleasure in the final stage of the sexual act. Many consider coitus as a necessity or duty, and give it up as soon as they can find a sufficient excuse for doing so without discrediting their self-respect. Others, on the other hand, continue perpetually trying new partners, believing that the fault is not theirs, and hoping to find the partner with whom the urge will be satisfied, and tension released with complete satisfaction.

Now let us see in a little more detail what exactly happens in the final stage of coitus. Friction and rhythmic movement bring excitation to a climax, at which the muscular walls of the excretory ducts passing from the testis to the ejaculatory ducts (vasa

[1] See *The Expression of the Emotions in Man and Animals* (John Murray, London), page 38.

deferentia) and the seminal vesicles, enter into rhythmic contractions, thus ejaculating spermatozoa and the secretions they
contain into the urethra. The semen, a mixture of spermatozoa
and secretions of the epididymis, the seminal vesicles, the pros-
tatic glands and the glands of Cowper, is ejaculated from the
urethra by rhythmical contractions of the bulbocavernosi (the
sphincter vaginae in the female) and the ischiocavernosi (the
erector clitoris in the female) muscles.

The complex reflex discharge of motor impulses of the whole
process is called orgasm. Most text books on physiology describe
coitus only in connection with impregnation. They go no further
than defining orgasm as the act of ejaculation in the male. Since
it is not necessary to impregnation, the question of female orgasm
is scarcely considered.   However, the sexual act in men is not
merely an act of procreation.   In modern society, the average
number of children is very small, while a conservative estimate of
the number of coiti in the lifetime of a normal couple is over five
thousand. The importance of sexual life before senility is such that
the question of impregnation itself may be completely divorced from
the sexual act in the context that concerns us at present.   And
for the same reason, it is essential to lay stress on the fact that in
the sexual act there is more complete equality between the sexes
than we are led to believe. Popular ideas of the active rôle being
played by the male, and of the passivity of the female are no more
than catch words. A normal mature woman is just as active as
the man, and often more so, throughout the act. It is true, of
course, that many women never mature to be active, but that is
due to the social status of women in our society, and their up-
bringing, and nothing else. A woman with mature personality,
affectionately disposed, uninhibited by shame, guilt or sinfulness,
is in all respects an equal partner in the act to the man.

In the sexual act, as in any act, there is a sensory, a motor and
emotive component. In some acts, one of the components may be
for practical reasons ignored. Not so in the sexual act. Here, the
act is incomplete and fails to achieve the biological reaction if
any of the components is even partially incomplete. A detailed
analysis is beyond the scope of the task we have set ourselves ; the
moral, aesthetic, social and other aspects are left out, not because
little importance is ascribed to them in the proper accomplishment
of the act, but because they are the subject of many excellent works.
Our problem is to show the rôle of the motor component which is
not self-evident, and is usually ignored.

In all cases where the sexual act is not terminated by a deep feeling of gratification, the reflex discharge of motor impulses is not proper. It is commonly understood that a sexual act is complete when ejaculation takes place. We have already pointed out the importance of examining not what is achieved in an act, but how things take place. In properly matured people, in all their functions, i.e., motor, libidinal and social, the excitement is built up to a climax at which involuntary rhythmic contractions in the muscles producing ejaculation spreads to the entire pelvic floor, and the pelvis itself rhythmically oscillates in the following manner. At each expulsion of semen, all the flexors of the abdomen contract powerfully and the pubis is pulled upward and forward to its utmost capacity, while all the extensors of the lumbar and sacral region are completely relaxed. Next, the pelvis withdraws so that the sacrum moves backwards and upwards again to the utmost capacity. The directions relate to the body in the normal upright standing position. The pelvis continues these oscillatory movements in synchronism with the successive emissions of semen. In both partners, facing each other, the pelvis movements relative to their own bodies are absolutely identical and coincide exactly. If they do not face each other, the forward movement of the male coincides with the backward movement of the female. The pelvic movements are part of the reflex discharge of motor impulses, and are as involuntary as the rhythmic contractions of the ejaculatory muscles, the erector clitoris or sphincter vaginae. The voluntary movements by which the friction of the penis and vagina walls is produced, are, to begin with, similar to any voluntary movements. Soon, however, with the excitement beginning to grow more rapidly, they become exactly co-ordinated in both partners, so when the reflex discharge starts, the oscillations of the pelvis only continue accentuated, and differ in nothing from the voluntary movements, but for the source and paths of the nervous impulses. The number of involuntary movements of the pelvis varies from three to seven or eight on the average.

This reflex part of the coitus can be carried out when the spinal cord is completely sectioned in the dorsal region, and all the impulses from the higher centres are cut off. For the centres regulating the reflex discharge, as well as those of erection, are situated in the lumbar and sacral spinal cord. The innervation of the sexual apparatus is very intricate.

Remembering the richness of the parasympathetic innervation of the sacral region, and the essential part the autonomous nervous system plays in the genitals, it is understandable that during intense excitation of the final stages of the sexual act, the pelvis, its floor and the lower abdomen participate in the reflex discharge. The pelvis is the locus where the amplitude of the oscillations is the greatest, decreasing all along the spine to die out at the base of the cranium.

The last movement is such as to draw the man and woman together, in which position they remain for some time before separating. In persons with no emotional trouble, in whom the act takes the form described, a deep feeling of tenderness and gratification follows a powerful involuntary breathing out which terminates the reflex phase of the act. All the muscles of the body, and especially the face, relax and express ease and well-being.

When the movements of the pelvis begin to become rhythmical, just before the reflex discharge takes over from the voluntary control, endearing, unintelligible utterances force their way out in both partners. Such a normal act is obviously only possible between persons having mutual attraction and understanding and between whom there are otherwise harmonious relations.

In short, only individuals fully matured in all their functions, mental, emotional, physical and social could so adjust themselves to each other as to make the sexual act an emotional, physical and aesthetic pleasure, mutually produced and equally shared. I have already insisted that arrested development in any function can be shown on all the planes simultaneously. In some, however, it is necessary to analyse abstract notions and use some sort of symbolic interpretation of words, while in others, where a sensory analysis is directly possible, there is a more direct and often easier way. As usual, therefore, we shall direct our attention to the anti-gravity activity, i.e., the motor muscular element.

The commonest, though perhaps the least important trouble is tiredness and stiffness in the lumbar region after coitus. This is not due only to " excesses," as some authors put it, for it often accompanies every single coitus, no matter how rare an event it may be. This stiffness is muscular, and is due to incomplete withdrawal of conscious control during orgasm. The pelvis is pulled powerfully by the violent reflective contraction of the abdominal flexors, while the lower spinal erectors are still held fixed in the habitual state of contraction. They are held short and are therefore stretched as the pubis is propelled forward and upward. Orgasm cannot be complete, as the reflex discharge is hindered by an habitual contraction of the pyriformis, the gemelli and the gluteals. The oscillations of the pelvis cannot have their full amplitude. Mechanically, there is a muscular component making the introduction of the penis incomplete. Mentally, there is the idea of withdrawal present in the mind. Incomplete amity, shame or guilt are present, interfering with that complete abandon of oneself normal to mature persons on such occasions. The social element of immaturity probably consists in realisation of personal dishonesty of some sort towards the partner.

Complete gratification is short-circuited by an element of anxiety which is conditioned with the habitual pattern of the musculature. The discharge tends to dissolve that pattern and so tends to bring the emotional conflict to conscious realisation. Indifference or disgust takes the place of gratification. Erection disappears sharply instead of very gradually. The sympathetic, with its inhibitory constrictive influence, replaces the vaso-dilatory influence of the parasympathetic which is associated with pleasure sensation.

Persons incapable of proper and complete gratification cannot easily reproduce even the voluntary oscillations of the pelvis when requested. Even when shyness and awkwardness are eliminated, they need guidance and example before they can reproduce pelvis motion in any way similar to the involuntary discharge. Most of the time it is the upward movement of the pelvis that is difficult or impossible. Thus, the muscular pattern of the movement reflectively elicited with each ejaculation of semen is foreign to their conscious idea or image of the act. When it tends to realise itself, there is a sense of apprehension of the unknown, similar to that which prevents people from losing consciousness. They regain complete conscious control at the expense of complete gratification.

In coitus interruptus, a similar process is consciously intended ; nevertheless, lumbar stiffness is the necessary result. Disgust may not follow the interrupted gratification. Sometimes, only the intensity of gratification is reduced. In any case, the affectionate attitude towards the partner gradually diminishes into indifference. All the mental, emotional, physical and moral elements enumerated above can be distinguished in coitus interruptus. They produce the same result, but perhaps more gradually, and with attenuated intensity.

It is understandable now why psychiatric treatment furthering emotional development, or adjusting the social relations of the partners, as well as physical re-education, will all have a partially

beneficial influence. The slowness, indirectness and incompleteness of the effect of any method alone, however, is obvious. For
altering one element (albeit an important one) of a complete act,
and leaving the other unaltered, makes learning of the new mode
very slow and problematical. So much of the old pattern is con-
tinued with the new mode of doing, that extinction of the unwanted element is performed in very unfavourable conditions.
Relapses to the complete old habitual mode of doing are inevitable, as the bulk of the old situation is present continuously and
tends to restore the old act in its completeness.

The antigravity motor link, the emotional, social and physical
elements of the sexual function, are all necessary to make a coherent picture. No element can be ignored without complete loss
of perspective. A function, like a picture, has no meaning if either
painter, canvas or painting are arbitrarily selected to be the most
significant. There is no function which has necessitated apprenticeship in which the somatic, motor, emotive or mental element
can be singled out as the cause of the others. Obviously, at different stages of maturity of the function, one of the elements may
seem to be more striking. The somatic element is indispensable
at the initial lowest level of the function. But once all the other
elements have been integrated during the maturing process of
the functions, only the most absolute destruction of the whole will
completely destroy all the elements of the function. We will
return to this most important aspect of our problem later.

It might be argued that, in spite of what was said in the last
paragraph, I do, in fact, attribute to the sexual function undue
dependence on muscular habit, and that I advance a somatic
element as the cause of it all. There is no predetermined, fixed
cause-and-effect correspondence between any voluntary muscular
pattern of the lumbar region—or any other region, for that matter
—and orgasm (or the sexual act in general) that is common to all,
and independent of individual experience. It is incorrect, therefore, to say that all persons with hyperextended pelvis are incapable of complete orgasm. Just as it is incorrect to say that a
person who habitually contracts his facial muscles to express
sorrow and despair is incapable of being gay, or that all people
who have a sad expression are sad for the same reason.

The essentially personal correspondence formed by personal
motor sensory experience thus stands out unambiguously. We
have also seen that the reflex discharge of motor impulses is not
affected by the relative position of the partners. It is immaterial

whether they face in the same direction or face each other. In the first case, the oscillations of the female pelvis are 180 degrees out of phase compared with those of the other situation. This again shows that there is no intrinsically inherent correspondence between muscular pattern and a specific emotional state, which is independent of personal experience. There is, however, a learned functional correspondence between every muscular pattern, the precise nature of which can be established only in each individual case. Because of recurrent environmental situations, certain correspondences become more probable, but there is nothing intrinsically fundamental which links negation, for instance, with right-left movements of the head. It is the most probable correspondence. Turks, however, express negation, by sharply lifting their heads.

The person with habitual immobility of the pelvis will obtain complete gratification in special conditions only. The conditions that are necessary and seem essential to him, will seem ridiculous to a mature person. He will fail every time he tries to change from his adjusted procedure. Many married couples remain faithful to each other because of inner conviction of sure failure with any major change in the process. Realising their dependence on the partner, they often struggle helplessly for independence. This manifests itself in an utterly irrational behaviour which destroys any tenderness that might have existed initially.

In perfect maturity, the reflex release of tension is complete and pleasurable. Potential perfection in any function is but rarely achieved. The majority of people are satisfied with something good enough to get along with. The further down we go towards the elementary stages of each function, the less numerous are the failures we encounter. The more serious the failure, the less frequent it is ; true biological impotence is very rare ; incomplete and indifferent orgasm very common. From this point of view, the next most common stage of immaturity is frigidity in women and premature ejaculation in men.

A very general feature of people suffering from premature ejaculation is partial inhibition of the extensors of the hip joints with the corresponding contraction of the adductors of the legs and flexors of the hips. The idea of penetration is correspondingly partially inhibited. Penetration is attempted, not by an inner urge, but by the circumstances developing to the stage where retreat will signify loss of face. Indeed, this is a central point of the complaint. Coitus, and, in particular, penetration, are not undertaken with the promise of satisfaction, but as a test for one's value. It is an attempt at self-assertion, produced by the intimate conviction of social failure in the plane most appreciated by the subject. The image of oneself losing face, or an exaggerated wish to show off, are extraneous ideas, completely out of place in the present circumstance. They are reinstated as part of an habitual pattern of doing. All the flexors are tense, breathing is halted as in all states of anxiety, the sympathetic system is overexcited; hence the incomplete and faltering erection; the face is tense, the jaws clenched. The general flexor contraction is found also in the hands. The subject has to make a conscious effort to stroke or caress the partner. If he does, it is with a deliberate intention to excite the partner, instead of the spontaneous tenderness felt in normal cases, together with the pleasure of doing so. His caresses are therefore clumsy and uninspiring; they are forced, short-lived and utterly inadequate. They are a mere caricature of what happens between two mature individuals.

Most people suffering from this complaint are gifted, sensitive people, far above the average. And the tragedy of the situation is that women are generally attracted to them by these qualities. The situation is aggravated by the fact that such men are usually generously endowed sexually. Once the improper manner of doing, acquired by ignorance and distorted emotional appreciation of reality, is replaced by one that allows maximum maturing of the personality, they prove to be above the average in all respects.

Through general faulty education arresting development, due to our ignorance, we form a false idea altogether of the function and act. There is nothing proper in the attitude, mentally, emotionally or physically. If closely examined, it is often found that the whole act does not come about because of any special mutual attraction, but was due to artificial, intellectually forced circumstances, more as the result of a decision to act than from sexual desire. A mature person in the same circumstances would remain completely cold and unruffled. The immature person thinks at once that he ought to be sexually excited, and forces himself into a situation for which he has no sincere desire. It is more surprising that he almost succeeds, in a fashion, than that his success is incomplete, laborious and tasteless.

Obviously, every one of the methods employed to remedy such situations can, and does produce improvement, and if there is any vitality left in the subject he may pick up and recover beyond what is warranted by the specific direct action of the method used. It is equally clear that the direct action on the total personality has a better chance of producing the desired result ; by reaching the lower and fundamental motor layers of self we facilitate a deeper reorganisation of the personality.

18. LOCALISATION OF FUNCTIONS AND MATURITY

THE growth of the nervous system is not uniform, and some parts grow much more quickly than others. The part of the system that is concerned with physiological processes and some reflex responses, is, on the whole, as complete at birth as in other animals. It is the cortex, the pyramidal tract and the rest of the nervous system which are instrumental in producing the enormous variety of highly differentiated intellectual and voluntary muscular activity of men. They continue to grow while external stimuli are arriving.

Thus, the individual experience of the first years of life is what really matters. To be more precise, it is the period before the pyramidal tract is more or less complete, and what happens during that time that will have the most profound effect on the whole manner of doing of the person. The muscular habits and the nervous connections that are formed while the baby learns to sit, walk and speak, influencing the growth and formation of the nervous patterns and analyser paths, will be the most difficult to change. They will form the pattern which the person will associate with his very self.

This is the reason why all evidence derived from psychoanalysis points to very early childhood as the source of symptoms of emotional trauma in the adult. The body and mind are never independent ; such subdivision is entirely arbitrary and unfounded. In some cases, the localisation is so diffuse that we can understand how the idea of soul or psyche grew. But the diffusion of localisation, when adequately understood, shows that the existence of a psyche, *per se*, in any way separable from the soma, is, to say the least, extremely unlikely. But we may, for the sake of convenience only, continue to group together all the functions of the human frame of diffused localisation and call them whatever we wish.

The subdivision of body and mind, soul or psyche is ancient, and was made when knowledge of functioning of the nervous system was nil. The complexity of the nervous system and its interaction with physiological process is great enough in itself, and we can ill afford to add to it primitively formed notions, which determine an approach to the problem in a biased frame of mind.

We know, in fact, so little about the functioning of the nervous system as a complete unit, that we have little right to expect any theory to be near the truth. We have to accept hypotheses that simplify the approach and point a direction for research in which some clarification of our ideas may be expected. By successive approximations, we may hope to arrive at some facts, instead of attractive, ingenious guesses.

Even the anatomy of the nervous system is not fully explored, and the knowledge of what goes on in some parts of the brain is practically nil. We cannot synthetise a single activity of the brain without admitting to conjectures, some plausible, others not, but none that can be completely relied upon.

The hind brain function is almost unknown. The cerebellum, which is a considerable part of it, and is anatomically an isolated unit in all vertebrates except amphibians, has been studied by Luciani, Orbeli,[1] Rademaker, and others. But all that is known for certain is that the cerebellum is closely connected with maintaining equilibrium. However, complete extirpation merely produces trouble in the function.

Orbeli thinks that the cerebellum helps to inhibit " old " activities of muscles—patterns that become redundant and are not to be used.

While it is usually understood that the psyche lodges in the frontal lobes, Claude Vincent's amputation of an entire prefrontal lobe of a patient, not only did not impair his psychic ability, but actually improved it. W. Penfield, who operated on his own sister, extirpated both frontal lobes, i.e., over a quarter of the entire encephalos, after which the patient, like many others who have undergone the same anatomically mutilating operation, could superficially be taken for normal. Dandy, Chorosko, Brickner and others have similar reports. So that, citing Paul Cossa's quotation of *Lhermite*, the deficit observed is " *défaut d'attention, de synthèse de mise en train, d'application pragmatique, enfin cette modification de la personalité dont le physionomie échappe à l'analyse, mais dont l'observateur attentif peut saisir l'ensemble s'il n'est pas dépourvu de tout sens psychologique.*" (Failure in attention, in synthesis, and in practical

[1] See *Lectures on the Physiology of the Nervous System*, 1935 (in Russian).

application and that indefinable change of personality which cannot nevertheless escape the careful observer unless he has no sense for psychology.)

Thus, only a careful observer with a trained sense can readily observe the result of the complete extirpation of where the psyche is supposed to be.

In this connection, it is interesting to remember Lashley's experiments. He taught rats to run complicated mazes, then enucleated both eye balls. The rats found their way through the mazes without difficulty. They forgot, however, what they had learned if parts of the brain were removed. The incapacity to perform the learned skill was found to be proportionate to the amount of brain removed, and independent of whether the eyes were enucleated or not.

He controlled his experiments by severing subcortically the association bundles, instead of extirpating the cerebral mass to which they are connected. The rats did not forget their lesson this time. Lashley concluded that the capacity for learning depends solely on the amount of cerebral mass undamaged, and on nothing else.

Dandy has, on five occasions, removed the whole right hemisphere of the brain in men, and found no psychic trouble resulting therefrom.

Zollinger had to remove the left hemisphere in a right-handed woman. After the operation she could pronounce five words only, in haphazard order. On the seventeenth day she began to improve, and her vocabulary showed a corresponding improvement.

This lack of localisation of higher functions in the cortex, and on the other hand, the punctual localisation of vision and hearing, is only another example of lack of simple anatomical principle in nature. Only by taking functioning as a guide can we make some coherent picture of the complexity of the nervous apparatus.

With so little firm ground, no theory can be formulated—only hypotheses ; the better hypotheses being the ones that give more guidance in more instances, and are more fruitful in showing where knowledge is lacking.

The idea of two lives, somatic and psychic, has in this respect outlived its usefulness. Since Freud, nothing of universal importance has been discovered in the psychic field in spite of great application and ingenuity.

Psychoanalysis, in Freud's writings at least, deals solely with psychic life. Only very rarely is there any allusion to the fact that psychic life does take place in a physical body. The unconscious, the *id*, the region of the pleasure principle with its repressions, nevertheless have a somatic support. In recent years, two new methods have been used for treatment of neurotics, namely, shock therapy and leucotomy, where an incision is made in the frontal lobe of the brain. These treatments often produce excellent results, even, as some practitioners assert, in schizophrenia. It is, therefore, a fact that a purely somatic action has, at least in some cases, the same effect as a psychoanalytic treatment. This in itself is sufficient to show that to speak of psychic life without connection with the soma is at the best a convenient abstraction, bound to spend its usefulness rapidly, as it did.

An hypothesis that gives some kind of explanation of how two so different methods as leucotomy and transference can produce the same result is therefore required. It is as follows :—

There is no fundamental difference of kind whatsoever between psychic and physical activity. Both disappear with the destruction of the nervous system, both are the outcome of its functioning. The immediately observable physical world is governed by definite laws. The permanency and constancy of these laws, and in particular of the law of gravity, have moulded the human mind and body to expect cause and effect relationship between all phenomena. So often can we see a cause prior to the effect that we expect a cause to every effect encountered. In body and mind relationship there has always existed a tendency to put one or the other as the cause, and make it more fundamental. For some, the body, i.e., the properties of the material support, the nervous system in particular, explains all human activity. For others, it is the mind that is essential, the body being an unworthy appendage with which we have to bear. We can find so many instances now confirming one point of view, now the other, that without being prejudiced it is difficult to form an opinion.

However, if we look more closely, and consider all the facts we have presented, some valuable conclusions can be drawn. First we observe that function is essential to life. Life without function of some sort seems to have no meaning. Next, we examine what sorts of function there are. At birth, all the functions that we observe are strictly localised in the body and in the nervous system. If we destroy, at birth, the eye, or the optical nerve, or the optical area in the cortex, the function is completely destroyed. No visual concepts, no visual memory, no visual images, no optical righting or standing reflexes will be observable at any time during the life of such an individual. At times, it may seem that such a person still has some notion of visual description. He may, for instance, refer to brightness of some sensation. This is only apparent. It is almost certain that brightness is a quality common to all senses. Only the word happens to be taken from our optical vocabulary. There is a quality of sound we cannot describe otherwise than as bright.

On the whole, it may be said that, at that level of maturity, the visual function is as strictly localised as our critical sense of correctness requires. The same argument applies to all the functions present at birth. At that level of existence, the material support is the bearer of all functions, and their localisation has a point-to-point correspondence in the nervous system. At that stage, the body is the most representative part of the being. Nearly all a proud mother can say about her offspring is that a baby has been born and it weighs seven and a half pounds. One other thing can be said—namely, it is a girl or a boy. The evidence for that is entirely material. Without body evidence there is no means of observing any virile or feminine function. At death, when there are no functions observable, only the material support remains visible. All " soul " and mind phenomena connected with that body are now observable only in and by other bodies in whom functioning goes on.

Between these two extremes existence can be divided into levels. The points at which the levels may be fixed conveniently are the different stages of maturity of the particular function we may be considering.

Each function develops while the nervous system and its executive mechanism grow. The functions that are fully matured, or nearly so, at birth, remain strictly localised in the organs and in the nervous system. The breathing function, all the vegetative functions, the reaction to gravity, the circulation, in short, all the elements of functions that need little or no apprenticeship, and no further growth of their material support or the nervous tissue concerned, continue to be localised.

The localisation of all the functions that need growth of the body, and in particular those that need growth of the nervous tissue and apprenticeship, becomes more and more diffuse at each successive level of maturity. At maturity, all these functions are practically a property of the whole organism, and the destruction of any nervous mass or organ, no matter how great the mutilation may be, cannot completely eliminate or abolish the function.

Thus, once the function of locomotion has matured, it is necessary to proceed with the total destruction of the material support to make movement absolutely impossible. The localisation of the function of communication between one person and another, once matured, becomes perfectly independent of the particular material support usually connected with it. Thus, Mollaret and Bertrand describe[1] the following case : They kept under observation at the Salpetrière Hospital in Paris, a patient who, at the age of seventeen, became ill, and lost the voluntary use of every muscle in his body except those of the eyelids and eyeballs, which he could move up and down. For seventeen and a half years he lay in the hospital. By means of these two movements, communication was maintained with the patient, who had complete mental awareness. He would pick the programme he intended to listen to on the earphones provided for him. A whole series of experiments was conducted, and clear, intelligible answers were obtained from this living mummy.

No communication is possible, however, with a baby, in whom the material support is intact, but in whom the function of intelligence with other beings has never matured.

Once maturity is achieved, the localisation is so diffuse that the destruction of the sense organ or extirpation of considerable parts of the brain, eliminate only elements of the functions, but never abolish them altogether. Short of total destruction, only complete extinction of voluntary muscular control, more complete than the case of decerebrate rigidity just cited, could eliminate the function of communication with other people.

The sexual function, for instance, develops slowly, and matures much later in life. Castration practised in early childhood will completely change the future development of the sexual function. There will be no erection, no orgasm, no sexual urge. The material support and the function are strictly localised in the lower levels of existence. Castration of the adult, who has performed coitus, renders him incapable of reproduction only. He continues to have erection, sexual urge and orgasm, and if unaware of being

[1]See *L'Hypertonie de Décérébration chez l'Homme* (Masson & Cie).

different from others, he would probably be quite normal in his social relations.

I know of a case where a man was knocked unconscious in riots, and mutilated while in that state. The surgeon had to extirpate both testicles. The patient was assured that they were intact, but had had to be pushed up into the abdomen because of the destruction of the scrotum. Five years later he was still having normal intercourse and seemed quite normal.

The diffusion of localisation of a function in the nervous system does not mean, of course, that the function has an existence *per se*, entirely free from dependence on material support. All the glands develop and mature normally in the presence of normal testicles, and the motor patterns acquire the specific masculine character ; the sexual act having been performed once, there are the motor-sensory paths and connections necessary for doing it again. The localisation of the function grows around the senses and the muscular centres. Touching a woman evokes the response and the affective state by the same mechanism as any other conditioned reflex would. All the behaviour built up during the growth of the function has formed motor-sensory connections, and the elimination of the testicles abolishes only procreation, one element of the sexual function, but does not affect directly the connections formed.

Another example, of common occurrence. A person born deaf is also dumb. But a person becoming deaf later after the muscular patterns and nervous paths have been formed, is only affected by his immediate deafness, but as far as speech articulation is concerned, only the control of the volume of his voice may be defective.

It must be agreed that improper behaviour, such as that of emotionally troubled and immature people, is possible with an anatomically intact nervous system and soma. And if we do not assume that psychic phenomena occur in an attenuated medium of unknown description, where " mental processes " are possible outside a material support, the trouble must be in the functioning connections of the intact nervous system. And this is predominantly the result of learning and maturing.

Maturing usually conveys the idea of reaching a stationary stage where no further change takes place. This introduces an element of fixity which is contrary to the dynamics of life. What I understand by maturity, is the capacity of the individual to break up total situations of previous experience into parts, to reform them into a pattern most suitable to the present circumstances, i.e., the conscious control effectively becoming the overriding servo-mechanism of the nervous system. Maturity, in that sense, is an ideal state where the uniqueness of man, his capacity to form new responses, or to learn, has reached its ultimate perfection.

19. SUMMARY AND REVIEW

ANIMALS, even the anthropoid apes, are born with a brain nearer to its ultimate size than is man's brain at birth. The human brain at birth weighs about one fifth of that of the adult. All the mechanisms concerned with voluntary movements are very incompletely developed in the newly born human being ; most other mammals are, in this respect, comparatively advanced. In many cases, in the bovines, for instance, a quasi adult-like control of movements is present a few minutes after birth. Correspondingly, behaviour, in other mammals, is predominantly of an inherited reflex character : it is thus more stereotyped, more stable, with very slight, if any, individual differences. This behaviour is fixed, and the learning or acquisition of new responses is slow and, on the whole, of little significance for them.

In man, on the contrary, the brain grows and forms while he adjusts himself to life. The parts of the nervous system that develop after birth are connected with voluntary action, muscular or otherwise, and the actual motor patterns of the cortex are formed and deeply influenced by the actual individual experience. The human motor cortex is therefore unique in its reactions and no two of them are identical.

Most voluntary acts are thus due to nervous connections and paths that are essentially more temporary than the true congenitally inherited patterns of more reflective behaviour. Instincts in animals and man are therefore very different. In man, there is little that can be called instinctive ; neither the food instinct, nor the self-preservation instinct is so completely independent of individual experience as in other animals. The weakness of instinctive patterns of doing in man, and the long period of growth of the voluntary innervations, are mostly responsible for the infinite variety of ways of doing of the most fundamental and the most simple acts. Learning becomes the greatest and, indeed, the unique feature distinguishing man from the rest of the living universe.

The formation of new patterns out of the elements of total situations of earlier personal experience, in short, learning, is the distinctive human quality. It is also the foundation of imagination. Human learning is essentially different from reflex conditioning, which in man is only of relatively secondary importance. In conditioning, the closeness of the new stimulus to the unconditioned response is the most important factor in animal learning. Moreover the new stimulus must precede the old one. Immediate reward and punishment applied consistently can be said to have the same consequences as conditioning. Habits formed in this way must wear off in time unless the conditioning is sustained from time to time. Immediate reward or punishment has obviously little to do with behaviour disorders.

Human learning is intrinsically connected with imagination. Through the agency of imagination the time interval between the new stimulus and the unconditioned tension can be made forever simultaneous. Thus, if a child is punished for masturbation he avoids being seen doing it again. When he learns another way of relieving the body tension, for which he is not punished, he gives up masturbation. But if his imagination has been sufficiently impressed by his parents, on whom he is completely dependent, that such terrible things *which he cannot test, prove or disprove,* such as loss of memory, impotence, social degradation, etc., are the sure consequences of such wickedness, he may have in his own imagination the factor that will link guilt and punishment forever together. The punishment is now linked with the act and is evoked at the shortest interval. Only if he acquires a new act of learning, discrediting the authority of the parent, will the consequences not be disastrous. Otherwise it is only a question of which particular form the process will take in each individual, and the frequency of future situations that will reinstate the guilt/punishment idea. For better or for worse this process is at work in all of us. The impotent and the Don-Juan are both the result of it. Both are unhappy people produced by an ignorant social order and not by any inborn wickedness or fault in their brain or anatomy.

The outstanding quality of the human conscious innervations seems to be a unique capacity to form new nervous paths, associations and regroupings of interconnections. Those made while the pyramidal tract is growing are the most stable, but even these are more labile than in other animals.

Even such vegetative processes as eating and excreting, owing to intervention and guidance on the part of parents, are influenced to such an extent that the muscular patterns and attitudes involved are different from one individual to another, except for the purely

reflective congenital part which is common to all. Thus, for the same
act achieving the same end, the actual paths in the innervation of
the cortex and the basal ganglia are different from one individual
to another. There are not only different modes and different
rates of contraction, but often the use of different muscles altogether. The bowel-evacuation act is very instructive as an example, firstly because it is one of the nearest to a purely reflective
action and one might expect it to be the same in all men ; and
secondly because it is perhaps the most private act and should
therefore hardly be directly influenced by social conventions. It
could be preserved in its original, primitive and purely vegetative
form.

Yet even this act involves a social adjustment with attitudes,
emotional and muscular patterns that have a profound influence
on the whole being. In early infancy it is as purely a reflective act
as we can imagine. Soon after, however, the mother will begin to
withdraw the security which her presence brings to the child, and
leave him in isolated privacy. Then a bargaining system begins :
the mother expects and the child " gives " something which he
alone can produce and which is eagerly expected from him. He
soon learns to give freely and gain approval or to contain himself
when he is neglected. Immature persons who are unable to dissociate parts of earlier experience without reinstating the whole
situation, when faced with tasks where they have to give of themselves without being acknowledged, acting against their own will,
become angry, feel like chucking the whole thing, and often
impulsively do so. But when forcing themselves to proceed with
the task they often develop diarrhoea. In a similar way rebellious-
ness against authority which is consistently checked is associated
with chronic constipation.

Every emotion is, in one way or another, associated and linked
in the cortex with some muscular configuration and attitude
which has the same power of reinstating the whole situation as
the sensory, vegetative or imaginary activity.

We cannot ignore the fact that some adult guides our early
steps. We are dependent on the adult for longer than any animal
and more absolutely so. Dependence is the main weapon or
instrument of teaching. The important point is not the relative
merit or effectiveness of the method used, but the fact that the
establishment of the paths in the cortex analysers and basal ganglia are directed by forces from the outside, i.e., by the social
environment. In most of the acts taught to us, the insistence is on

a procedure similar to that which the adult considers to be satisfactory. He does not give us the means whereby to achieve the
end, but punishes or rewards us or, what is more important, makes
us punish or reward ourselves. Perhaps one of the most striking
examples of this sort is the teaching of not wetting the cot. No-
body knows what the baby is supposed to do to control a bodily
function. The child is urged in one way or another to do something
to itself, and to become master of its vegetative system—often
before he has even the rudiments of control of his voluntary
muscles.

One by one, slowly, all the normal functions will appear, but
none of them quite spontaneously. Some parents will pay more
attention to this or that activity, some to another, depending on
the age, the society and the knowledge prevailing at that time.

It is thus a matter of pure chance, with a large bias towards the
imitation of the adults concerned, as to which particular pattern
of doing the child will strive for, even in the best of cases. It is
most likely that he will adopt a particular manner of doing in
order to satisfy or imitate some adult.

Because of the incomplete development of our nervous system
in infancy, every act of learning is a laborious and slow process.
The adult is, therefore, often compelled to harden his heart and
insist on what he thinks is good for the child, and to take himself
as an example when he is in doubt. On the whole, then, most of
our learning processes are disagreeable. Repetition, however,
soon facilitates the flow of nervous impulses, as if the associated
paths straighten, deepen and become preferred. But in the great
variety of ways of achieving the same end, there are those which
suit our nervous system and executive organs and others that
suit them less well.

Because of the immense facility of adjustment in man, it is more
likely that the learned procedure is unfortunate than that the
inheritance is at fault. Especially when faults appear only after
many years in which nothing wrong could be detected by any
scientific examination. Thorndike gives diagrams of consecutive
states of synapses in the process of learning. According to him, the
arborisation of the neurons increases when the passage of impulses
is facilitated. Once such a facilitated path is formed, we have
acquired an habitual, preferred way of doing which we consider
our own. It is, however, doubtful whether this is really the whole
story. The fact that we can inhibit the facilitated path shows that

the centres of higher level of the nervous organisation must be involved.

J. Z. Young[1] suggests the following mechanism for simple learning. Let an unconditioned stimulus A, normally produce a motor response M, while the stimulation of another pathway B, does not produce any response of M though connected to M by nervous fibres. The stimulation of A and B together not only produces the motor response in M, but also excites the common circuits. The cycle continues to work after the stimulus has ceased, and this reduces the threshold of M so that it will next respond to the weaker excitation of B alone. There is a likelihood that something of this sort actually occurs in the higher centres.

Many of our failings, physical and mental, need not therefore be considered as diseases to be cured, nor an unfortunate trait of character for they are neither. They are an acquired result of a learned faulty mode of doing. The body only executes what the nervous system makes it do. It moulds itself during growth for a longer period, and to a greater extent, than in any other animal. Actions repeated innumerable times for years on end, such as all our habitual actions, mould even the bones, let alone the muscular envelope. The physical faults that appear in our body long after we were born are mainly the result of activity we have imposed on it. Faulty modes of standing and walking produce flat feet, and it is the mode of standing and walking that must be corrected, and not the feet. The extent to which our frame is able to adjust itself to the use and requirements we make of it seems to be limitless ; by learning a better use of control, the feet, the eyes, or whatever organ it may be, will again adjust themselves and change their shape and function accordingly. The transformations that can be produced, and their rapidity, sometimes border on the incredible.

Our ways of doing are acquired by repetition to which either tacit or conscious consent is given each time. We soon begin to feel right with them, and then quite incapable of changing them. Sooner or later we begin to consider those particular modes of doing to be the only ones possible, and they become part and parcel of our very self. Because of the repeated consent given, habits become immune to criticism by others from within and quite impervious to correction ; they have become a feeling, and as such unassailable.

A striking example is the phenomenon of " sensitive feet." It

[1] *Evolution* (Oxford, 1936).

illustrates, at the same time, arrested learning in the gravity function. Some people never learn to walk properly in shoes. The heels introduce an extra difficulty, as they alter the relation between most of the bones and muscles of the body, from that which would exist without them. The important point is that some people never make that adjustment perfectly. How important this faulty adjustment may be, only those who suffer from it can tell. That suffering could arise in such a manner is, at first sight, astonishing. A person walking barefoot learns readily not to step so that pain results. In shoes, however, the position is different. Some people have corns, bunions and other malformations that are so painful that they dare not touch them themselves. These malformations are often of such long standing, sometimes several decades, that the bone process itself is altered in structure. It is understandable that a ready-made shoe may not fit properly, that one wants to have a smart-looking foot, and therefore buys shoes that do not quite fit and that must be worn out before new ones can be bought ; but it is hardly probable or plausible that for thirty years all shoes have just the requisite faults to press on the same point exactly. We exclude, of course, those who have a congenital malformation, who do not fall into the category of people we are discussing. Obviously, therefore, the fault is not with the shoes but with the manner of putting the foot to the ground. When excessive pressure is repeatedly brought to bear on a small area of the skin, a water blister is formed. In spite of the pain, the foot continues to be put in the same way with the weight of the body bearing on the same irritated point. Often a corn is removed but soon grows again, as the subject continues his obviously faulty manner of doing. He is incapable of learning a new manner of use of the foot, even with such a merciless teacher as pain.

A decerebrated animal withdraws its limb when pinched or pricked. A sleeping man, too, withdraws his leg if a painful stimulus is applied to it. This is done reflectively, and if withdrawal is prevented, the man wakes up. Obviously, therefore, it is the conscious overriding control that inhibits the lower centres from withdrawing the foot from the painful position. Normally, one learns from experience, by correcting earlier patterns of behaviour. When a person continues to use a stereotyped pattern of behaviour instead of one suitable to the present reality, the learning process has come to a standstill. Some authors define neurosis as a series of stereotyped reactions to problems that the person has never solved in the past, and is still unable to solve in the present. A person continuing to have corns in the same place with different shoes is showing elements of neurotic behaviour.

Observation shows that people who suffer chronically from the complaint described, are often vain and extremely secretive about their body; that they stubbornly refuse change; they are irritable and despotic at home but affable and helpful to strangers. The incapacity to make adjustments to the environment manifests itself in many other activities. The subject prefers his own way of doing, no matter what the result may be. With such a disposition he is bound to get into deep waters. He has no feet to stand on, so his attitude to authority is yielding. All his authority appears when he puts his slippers on ; so pity his wife ! He knows better than anybody else, but " they " do not appreciate him etc., etc.

Two capital points running all through our exposition are illustrated hereby. First, that maturity, means that the individual has learned to bring to bear upon the present circumstance only those parts of previous experience that he consciously deems necessary. The immature person cannot stop himself from restoring the whole situation where only an element of it is associated with the present. Second, that to re-educate, perfectly and successfully, a person such as the one described, by psychiatric methods alone, is a forlorn hope. Such treatment cannot have any lasting effect. The psychiatrist will treat emotional instability, will make him relive the old trauma of childhood, and will obtain an apparent improvement, restoring possibly failing potency, etc., but so long as no radical change of the nervous and body patterns has been wrought, any sharp change of environment, any new shock, or simply time will, by dint of the unchanged muscular and attitudinal patterns, reinstate the whole situation, and bring back the old manner of doing with only minor differences of detail, every time treatment is given up.

The anxiety pattern, integrated on the peculiar attitudes of the body, and especially in the muscular habits of the face, neck, pelvis and feet of the subject, will very often be reinstated. So long as direct dissolution of the immature muscular patterns has not been achieved. And to achieve this, a better substitute pattern must be provided. The subject cannot afford to, and will not, part with his habitual mode of doing, which feels right, before he has learned one that " feels " at least equally right. Emotional re-education alone, though of immense help, will only indirectly, and therefore only occasionally, provide the subject with feet that are not painful in every unexpected step. Such feet often stand in the way of complete recovery, as they repeatedly reinstate the old state of anxiety, and bring to a standstill the psychiatrist's efforts. To get rid of this and similar obstacles to potential maturity, the whole personality, including the antigravity function, must be relearned and adequately adjusted.

Even in pure psychiatric treatment, the somatic element plays a much greater part than is realised. Freud's use of the couch on which the patient lies, is especially significant. It was intended to make the patient comfortable. In the light of the importance ascribed to habitual muscular patterns, in that they reinstate the vegetative states conditioned with them, the partial elimination of the effect of gravity has a greater value than simple comfort. In fact, the patient often curls up—that is, flexes all his articulations in a position reminiscent of the one we have described as synonymous with safety, except that he lies on his side. With this partial elimination of gravity, the habitual muscular patterns are eliminated and spontaneous anxiety abated. Anxiety will now have to be brought about by associations and emotional reactions, and is thus dissociated from the habitual carriage of the body.

The psychiatrist himself judges the patient by his body more than he realises. Thus, when the door opens, the first movements of the person entering tell him at once whether he has to do with a patient or with a newspaper reporter who has come to interview him. With prolonged experience, he often even forms a shrewd guess at the patient's complaint solely by the carriage and movements of the patient, i.e., solely by the gravity adaptation of the patient.

I contend that the cures achieved by " purely " psychiatric treatment, which are satisfactory, are those in which the muscular patterns have been corrected indirectly, by chance. Fortunately, for the reasons explained, this is not impossible, nor rare, but it is uncertain, and recovery is never as complete as it could otherwise be. Direct attention to the soma and psyche makes complete functional maturity possible ; moreover, re-education is considerably facilitated, hastened, and made to last—or, less dogmatically, has a better chance of lasting.

Re-education of the kinaesthetic sense, and resetting it to the normal course of self-adjusting improvement of all muscular activity—the essence of life—is fundamental. By the principle of correlation, it has the advantage of directly improving breathing, digestion and the sympathetic and parasympathetic balance, so important in the sexual function, all linked together with emotional experience and is a worth-while enterprise in its own right at any time. The outstanding feature is, however, that the muscular anxiety pattern is broken up by a proper distribution of habitual tone between flexors and antigravity muscles, thus giving the psychiatrist an efficient and direct tool by clearing up the body foundations of the " central problem of neuroses." Moreover, by eliminating contraction and rigidity in the pelvic region, an obstacle interfering with reflex discharge of motor impulses, essential to normal orgastic release of tension in the sexual act, is removed ; the way to complete maturity, sexual and otherwise, is cleared. To achieve anything as direct as this by emotional re-education alone is just as feasible as curing a neurotic by " physical jerks " alone.

Motility seems to be more elementary because it is essential to the lowest level of existence. In certain cases, it is therefore the only part of the personality that is amenable to re-education at all. Psychiatric emotional re-education of an illiterate individual with a limited vocabulary of abstract terms is, in fact, a thankless job. The following is a case in point.

An illiterate foreigner complains of sexual failure which he describes expressively by gesture. Analysis being based on verbal communication finds itself in this case deprived of the means of finding out anything about the past emotional history of the subject. Even if it could be done, the analyst would have to put himself into the setting of customs, traditions and moral background of the subject before he could give any rational guidance. In complete contrast, the body and motility diagnosis needs no verbal communication at all ; re-education can be taught by example alone. And with the re-education of the motor function, a great deal of the road to complete recovery has been covered. In constantly altering environment, all-round maturity is necessary to ensure a continuing satisfactory integration of the self for the immediate purpose or event.

Miss P. Locatelli has shown[1] that the nervous cells are the primary factor responsible for the formation of the segments that they innervate. She has isolated the sciatic nerve of a triton and bent it on to the back muscles, then amputated the corresponding leg. After about two months, the protuberance formed at the spot where the nerve was planted, grew into a robust limb with three fingers, as in a normal leg. Though not all experiments were

[1] See pages 279–282 of *Com Re. de l'Assoc. des Anatomist* (Turin, 1925).

so successful, even the failures were more or less reminiscent of the member in question.

Even more striking are P. Weiss's experiments.[1] He transplanted pieces of spinal cord of one salamander larva to another, as well as a leg, so that nerve fibres grew into it. When this happened, the muscles of the limb began to contract ; they would not, however, respond to stimulation of the skin. This shows that the nervous tissue produces its own activity without being excited by external stimuli. Later, when also sensory connections were formed, reflex activity could be elicited. Thus nerve cells discharge impulses spontaneously without external provocation, so to speak. It is conceivable that some of the unsolved problems of nervous functioning will finally be elucidated along these lines.

The nervous system is not solely a passive reactor that remains quiescent when no stimuli from the environment impinge on it ; it has a very important activity of its own, of which we unfortunately know very little. One thing seems to be established beyond doubt, namely, that the previous history of a particular nervous system, i.e., the kind of irritations it has actually undergone, has the most profound influence on its biological properties. We have mentioned one such irritation—Speransky's massage of the brain, produced by alternate withdrawal and re-introduction of the cerebro-spinal fluid. Owing to the unique capacity of man to form new responses, the kind of irritations to which every nervous system is submitted, varies from individual to individual. The responses of each nervous system are therefore different even to identical physical, chemical or any other stimuli. The implications of this uniqueness of man are greater than could be suspected. Closer scrutiny throws a singular light on human nature and behaviour.

Until birth, the total of differentiated impulses that has reached the nervous system is negligible. Minkowski and others have shown that the nervous activity in the foetus is extremely diffuse and lacks definition. It is possible that this is not quite so in cases of trauma to the mother during pregnancy.[2] The stimuli reaching the nervous system of the foetus through the outer envelope of its body are uniform, changing slowly and between narrow limits.

When a baby is born, we can tell very little about him ; we

[1]*Proc Amer. Phil. Soc.*, 1941, *84.* 53.
[2]See Marfan's *Maladies des Enfants*—chapter on congenital and hereditary sources of nervous disorders in infants.

can tell his weight, whether his body is firm or flabby, his colour normal, how his heart beats, and so on. On the whole, only somatic and vegetative descriptions can be given. By these characteristics, a pediatrist of experience may venture a guess as to what kind of person will grow out of the body, especially if he knows both parents.

We cannot tell whether the infant has any idea of space, time, form or any other concept that we associate with conscious awareness. Judging by his reactions now and later, it is safe to say that he has not the faintest idea of such things. On the other hand, a fairly shrewd idea can be formed by the specialist of all his vegetative and body functions.

In short, no trace of what we call character, or human nature can, at this stage, be detected.

As soon as the baby is born he begins to breathe, and the reaction to falling can at once be elicited.[1] These are the foundations of motility. Muscular contraction and breathing are intimately related in the nervous system, as can be seen in such simple facts as the return to normal length of a stretched muscle in steps synchronous with the breathing rhythm. As soon as a baby enters the world, he becomes subject to the effect of gravity, from which he was largely free while he was immersed in a liquid of approximately his own density.

On top of the exteroceptive and proprioceptive mechanisms, the labyrinth is the chief antigravity organ. This organ, and in particular the vestibular apparatus, is instrumental in forming our spatial and temporal relations with the outside world. The labyrinth has a strong influence on the vegetative nervous system. Pallor of the face, nausea, vomiting, nystagmus of the eyes, change of tone of the blood vessels and complete inhibition of all the extensors, are the result of a few rotations of the untrained labyrinth.

On these foundations of motility all the motor acts will gradually build up : first, the reaction to falling ; crying appears at sharp movements or withdrawal of support, or in certain states of the digestive tract : secondly, the contraction of the tensor tympani ; loud noises start a reflex deglutition or swallowing to equalise the pressure in the middle ear with that outside.

The first motor acts are thus elicited on a background of intense vegetative reactions. Also, the first sensory impulses eliciting

[1] See M. Bergeron, *Les Manifestations Motrices Spontannées chez l'Enfant* (Herman & Cie, Paris).

these acts are thus conditioned with special vegetative states. From now on, the number and variety of sensory reactions will steadily increase, in all sorts of possible combinations, to form our awareness in waking activity. The growth of the pyramidal tract and the rapidly developing higher integrating centres of the cortex and the basal ganglia, will soon become apparent in the gradually maturing voluntary conscious activity of the growing man.

All this activity of the nervous system is essentially the result of individual experience, and is the direct effect of social environment on it. In this activity, consisting predominantly of stimuli reaching the nervous system through the envelope of the body, i.e., through the senses, all sensations are related to phenomena governed by strict causality. They can be classified logically, and a complete account can rationally be given of them from one person to another. At the moment of birth, the total number of such events and sensations that has reached and impressed the nervous system is practically nil. The conscious activity at that moment is correspondingly equally negligible.

On the other hand, reactions taking place inside the boundary of the body, and sensations to which they give rise, those of the muscles and the rest of the executive mechanism associated with motor acts, do not obey the laws of causality as strictly as the former. The mechanism of transmission of impulses from viscera, glands, vessels etc. consists of chemical substances diffusing through a mass of different media, membranes and liquids, which, themselves, continually alter the rate and character of transmission of nervous excitation.

The topographical configuration here becomes a more important factor than anything else. The temporal sequence of the events is not preserved, and impulses may reach the integrating centres in any order, depending entirely on the distance and route they have travelled to reach that centre. Therefore, sensations resulting from identical stimuli at different moments may elicit quite different reactions ; in the interval between them a change may have occurred because another reaction may alter not only the speed of transmission, but the state of the integrating centres themselves. This constitutes what Speransky calls an irritation, after which the response of the nervous system may be entirely new.

The non-repetitive character of such reactions, the absence of linear temporal sequence, and the resulting absence of causal relationship between stimuli and sensation, make all communication between persons on this subject vague and uncertain. No rational, logical structure can be established without a repetitive spatial and temporal order.

Stimuli arising from the environment reach the integrating centres of the nervous system through the teleceptors or the muscles ; the impulses travel through medullated nerves and the delays in arrival, are strictly fixed, and in general very short.

There is a distinct difference between the two kinds of reactions, from every point of view. For instance, the patterns formed before birth, and those appearing immediately after, are as permanent as the vegetative processes. Thus, the first reaction to gravity, stimulation of the flexors, inhibition of the extensors, and halting of breath, will remain unaltered all through life, and will be elicited with every sudden strong stimulus. Old reflex patterns show up easily when the conscious control is engaged in performing an act. If a person extending his arm to get hold of something, is interrupted by a loud shout he will flex the arm and fail to accomplish his intended act. If the shout occurs while he is flexing his arm, after having deposited something, he will not extend it, but will flex it more violently. In either case, there will be a break in the breathing rhythm. The frightening stimulus does not simply reverse the performed act, nor halt it, but the old pattern of the reaction to falling which is elicited by the loud noise is superimposed on to the present act. Patterns acquired later in life are so much less permanent, that if we do not use them for any length of time, we need a special effort to repeat them, and we feel as if we have to learn them anew.

The pre-natal reactions are a genetic inheritance, common to all of us, and are similar to those of other animals ; those acquired through sensory experience are essentially personal.

Our reflex activity consists predominantly of genetically inherited reactions, and is only sluggishly and slightly influenced by individual experience. Any such influence coming from the outside world cannot reach the nervous system otherwise than through the senses, and always involves some muscular activity.

The motor cortex is therefore the common axis on which both the conscious and reflex reactions are hinged ; and no permanently altered reaction to any environmental stimuli can rationally be expected without a rearranged muscular response.

It is remarkable that we have not had to use the idea of the Unconscious throughout our exposition. The motor link, binding together sensory and vegetative experience in the higher nervous centres, explains easily facts remaining obscure, or for which elaborate, far-fetched explanations are given. People suffering from chronic premature ejaculation, for instance, do so also in their dreams. It is difficult to understand why a subject should not dream normal gratification when conscious control is dormant, if the dream is a manifestation of an " unconscious " wish fulfilment. An " instinctive " love for pain and torture, of equal importance to the love of pleasure, must be accepted to explain such elements in dreams if an Unconscious is assumed. If, however, the motor centres are considered as the binding link between body reaction and activity, it is obvious indeed that the vegetative state will elicit the muscular patterns habitual to the subject and vice versa, by the same mechanism as spontaneous and voluntary mimicry. The premature ejaculation is not the normal reflective orgasm involving muscular activity in a congenitally inherent pattern, but is its substitute, modified by individual experience. The habitual orgasm pattern is reinstated, and replaces all others for which there is no facilitated path.

When the habitual manner is dissolved, normal gratification is dreamed. It is easier to conceive altered motor patterns, as in normal learning, rather than modifications in an "Unconscious" which must be, to be of any use, a set of innate, inheritable and essentially unalterable drives common to all. What we observe is shapeless biological tensions ; the form they take depends entirely on the personal experience. The form is similar only in the same social order and is the result of it.

20. CONCLUSIONS

A CLEAR distinction should be made between conditioning in animals and learning in men, as well as between adaptation, which is an evolutionary process correlating whole species to an environment, and adjustment through which individuals fit themselves to particular circumstances of more temporary nature.

Behaviour disorders arise through the adjustment of the individual to a specific given social order and have little to do with the biological adaptation and species character. Properly handled, cripples of all description become expanding and creative adults ; examples are so numerous that it is superfluous to name any.

Neuroses can be produced only in domesticated laboratory animals in which dependence on human beings has been developed and flight excluded. In men, too, utter dependence on the adult is the essential condition of teaching the child ; without it there is no room for punishment or reward. In all behaviour disorders there is of necessity an element of lack of security which only an utterly dependent being could have experienced after withdrawal of the protection and affection to which it has been accustomed.

Physical punishment following the unwanted act, provided it is not violent enough to compromise existence, has, on the whole, little to do with behaviour disorders. It may create fear and the subject will learn to conceal or abstain from the act. Anxiety is, however, associated with human learning through a vicious circle of guilt and self-punishment, threats of personal depravity and degradation, doom and after-death punishment, that cannot be proved or disproved by the child and creates conflict. Thanks to imagination we have a merciless teacher in ourselves who is forever there and from whom we can conceal nothing. The essential factor of conditioning and habit formation, the time interval between the new and old stimuli, is made as short as possible.

This process is now understood in many quarters. Already the present growing generation is spared much futile suffering and shows signs of greater emotional stability, With healthier and saner teachers and moralists the future generations have a good chance of forming a happier disposition altogether.

To help ourselves, the victims of the passing social order, it is essential to realise fully that emotional instability and behaviour disorders are the result of faulty and exaggerated technique of habit formation. Even the motor activity, which is the centre of all activity, has been shown in the preceding pages to be considerably different in men and formed by the personal adjustment to the actual social and physical environment. In the ultimate analysis it is little different from other habit formations.

Radical changes cannot be expected without reforming muscular and postural habits. Indigestion, faulty breathing, crooked toes and feet, faulty sexual behaviour, postural rigidity and muscular tension go together with emotional disorders. The whole self, diet, breathing, sex, muscular and postural habits, must be tackled directly and concurrently with the emotional re-education.

The whole problem is a social one and re-education has much better prospects of success if conducted in groups and not in the seclusion and pretended secrecy of the consulting room. It should start with muscular and postural re-education on the lines we have already discussed. Many students will find sufficient relief in this alone and, helped by clearer understanding of the process of habit formation, may be able to further their maturing process by their own means. The edge of anxiety is blunted by the dissolution of the anxiety patterns, not in isolation but in a community and without disclosure of details of personal experience even to the teacher. Those who need it are free to seek individual attention. The number of silent sufferers who dread the consulting room and cannot afford it, is far greater than is generally realised. The group joined primarily for physical re-education solves the two problems ; the whole procedure is that of adult re-education and not treatment. This it should be, for it is a question of teaching and learning and not of disease and cure.

INDEX